Focus on U.S. History:

The Era of Revolution and Nation-Forming

Kathy Sammis

J. WESTON

WALCH

PUBLISHER

Portland, Maine

User's Guide
to
Walch Reproducible Books

As part of our general effort to provide educational materials which are as practical and economical as possible, we have designated this publication a "reproducible book." The designation means that purchase of the book includes purchase of the right to limited reproduction of all pages on which this symbol appears:

Here is the basic Walch policy: We grant to individual purchasers of this book the right to make sufficient copies of reproducible pages for use by all students of a single teacher. This permission is limited to a single teacher, and does not apply to entire schools or school systems, so institutions purchasing the book should pass the permission on to a single teacher. Copying of the book or its parts for resale is prohibited.

Any questions regarding this policy or requests to purchase further reproduction rights should be addressed to:

Permissions Editor
J. Weston Walch, Publisher
321 Valley Street • P. O. Box 658
Portland, Maine 04104-0658

1   2   3   4   5   6   7   8   9   10
ISBN 0-8251-3336-X

Copyright © 1997
J. Weston Walch, Publisher
P. O. Box 658 • Portland, Maine 04104-0658

Printed in the United States of America

CONTENTS

UNIT 3. CHANGING AMERICAN SOCIETY

UNIT 4. CREATING NEW GOVERNMENTS

UNIT 5. FINE-TUNING THE SYSTEM

CREDITS

Dover Pictorial Archive   *vii, viii, ix,* 1, 3, 4, 5, 7, 8, 9, 10, 11, 12, 13, 14, 15, 16, 17, 18, 21, 22, 23, 24, 25, 26, 27, 28, 30, 32, 33, 34, 36, 37, 38, 42, 43, 44, 45, 46, 49, 50, 51, 52, 54, 57, 61, 62, 64, 67, 69, 70, 74, 75, 76, 77, 79, 80, 84, 87, 92

North Wind Picture Archives   19, 20

Corel Corporation CD   92

TO THE TEACHER

The era of the American Revolution and the years following it, when the new nation formed its political institutions and government structures, are of critical importance in the study of U.S. history. The thirteen colonies became the United States of America. The revolutionary ideas spawned new republican governments, and these ideas and governments inspired many more revolutions and changes in government around the world for years, even centuries, to come. The spirit of equality and independence likewise inspired changes in society and politics and promoted a spirit of reform that still animates American life. In studying this era, students will gain an understanding of the ideas on which our nation was founded and on which it still rests, as well as how and why our national government, economy, and political institutions were formed.

The reproducible student activities in this book draw students into the experience of revolution and nation building, to help them develop a rich understanding of what shaped the political and social structures of present-day life. Many activities in this book use original-source documents. Sharing the reactions and thoughts of real people who experienced pivotal events brings history to life. Reading portions of important original documents, such as the Bill of Rights and the Articles of Confederation, makes them also real, not just abstract concepts.

Organization

Student activities are divided into units that follow the National Standards for History. Each unit begins with several background pages that give students information relevant to the unit topic. A number of reproducible activity pages follow, including reading selections from original contemporary sources and decision making, comprehension, analytical, comparative, chronological, interpretive, research, mapping and graphing, role-playing, interactive, and interdisciplinary activities.

Each unit includes some extra challenge activities, enrichment for more advanced or adventurous students. Activities based on time lines reinforce chronology, as they draw students into broader descriptive and illustrative areas. Maps are provided as needed within units. The main map of eastern North America, which is used in four of the five units, follows this introductory material. You may copy it as needed.

Each unit is preceded by a teacher guide that gives an overview of the unit and its objectives, plus specific teaching suggestions for each student activity.

Lower-level students may have difficulty reading the original-source documents, with their old-fashioned words and syntax. You might want to go over original source selections in class to be sure that all students fully comprehend them.

At the end of the book, you'll find a section titled Answer Key, Additional Activities, Assessments that has answers for the student activities, suggested additional activities, and at least one assessment vehicle for each unit. The resource section lists fiction and nonfiction books, as well as resources and enrichment materials in other media. The glossary is reproducible for student use.

TO THE STUDENT

The American Revolution gave birth to the United States of America. Before the Revolution, the nation was a group of loosely connected colonies. Great Britain "owned" the colonies and ruled them. During the 1600's and the early 1700's, England didn't pay a lot of attention to the colonies. The mother country was busy fighting with European rivals, so Americans got quite used to running their own affairs.

When peace came, England changed its colonial policy. It tightened its control over the colonies. It taxed the colonists. It interfered with the colonists' self-government. The colonists thought England was trampling on their rights. They objected, loudly. They rioted. They dumped tea into Boston Harbor. But Britain and its king wouldn't relax their hard line. Finally, British soldiers and American soldiers began shooting at each other in two small Massachusetts villages. The war lasted seven long years, but the colonies won, and a new nation was born.

The nation was founded on the spirit of equality and independence. That spirit would spread around the world in years to come. It also spread through American society and remains a force for reform in our present-day world.

With the new nation came new governments, national and state. The world hadn't seen anything like this before. Common people were getting together and creating new republican governments for themselves! We're still living under those same governments and political institutions today, more than 200 years later.

The activities you'll do for this course of study will help you better understand this era of revolution and nation forming. You'll work with maps and graphs. You'll put yourself in the shoes of revolutionary-era people, deciding whether to support the Revolution or the king, debating a thorny constitutional question, choosing a political party. You'll read what revolutionary-era people had to say about their lives. You'll also read some original documents whose provisions still apply to your life today. When you're finished, you'll have a better grasp of how the United States came into existence, why it took the form that it did, and how its institutions were created and grew.

Name _____

Date _____

Map: Eastern North America

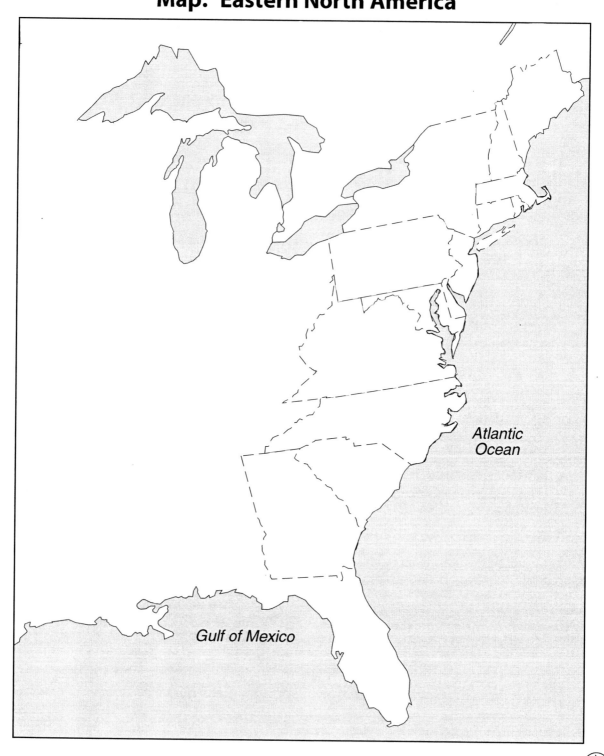

Atlantic
Ocean

Gulf of Mexico

x

Focus on U.S. History:
The Era of Revolution and Nation-Forming

The Road to War

The objectives of this unit are for students to understand what caused the American Revolution and the principles set forth in the Declaration of Independence. English imperial policy toward the colonies changed when the Treaty of Paris ended the war with the French in 1763. This new, more intrusive imperial policy sparked debate in the colonies about rights to representation and freedom from taxation. A chain of British imperial moves and colonial protests ultimately led colonials to debate the question of declaring independence from the mother country. Even after the Revolutionary War started at Lexington and Concord in April 1775, that question was still unresolved. Delegates at the Second Continental Congress made the fateful decision on July 2, 1776. Thomas Jefferson enunciated the colonists' justifications for their split with Great Britain in the Declaration of Independence, adopted on July 4, 1776. The activities in this unit are designed to help students understand these aspects of the road to revolution in the colonies.

Student Activities

The Peace of Paris shows students visually how colonial territory changed hands with the Treaty of Paris in 1763. The Extra Challenge offers students another way to visualize the changes by creating contrasting maps of eastern North America before and after the French and Indian (Seven Years') War.

Steps to Revolution challenges students to arrange major events leading up to the Revolution in chronological order, with the incentive of solving a word puzzle at the same time. Students then construct a time line showing these and other significant events in the chronology of the Revolution.

Voices of Dissent and **Voices of Consent** offer students original source quotes, from colonists who objected to British imperial policies and from colonists and Englishmen who supported the policies. Students use the readings to summarize the positions of both sides. Both summaries and readings are the basis for the next activity.

Loyalist or Patriot? has students imagine themselves as different colonists with particular interests and decide whether to support the Loyalist or the Patriot side. For an extra challenge, students can role-play a debate between Loyalists and Patriots.

One Event, Two Pairs of Eyes has students consider how various major events of the Revolutionary era would be differently described from the Patriot and from the Loyalist viewpoint.

Two Patriots presents the argument of Thomas Paine for independence from Great Britain and the argument of John Dickinson, a leading moderate Patriot, against independence. Students use these two views, as well as any others they have investigated, in role-playing a class debate about declaring independence.

Understanding the Declaration of Independence offers selected phrases from the Declaration of Independence. Students work in small groups to develop explanations of these phrases, which they share with the rest of the class.

Why Independence? presents the specific grievances set out in the Declaration that Jefferson used to justify breaking with Great Britain and its king. Students identify the actual events that Jefferson alluded to.

Slavery and the Declaration of Independence examines why a Declaration proclaiming equality, liberty, and inalienable rights failed to condemn slavery. Students study a paragraph condemning slavery and the slave trade that Jefferson originally included in the Declaration. After they decipher the difficult-to-read language, they explain why Jefferson dropped this condemnation paragraph in his final version of the Declaration.

The Road to War

War Ends and a New Policy Begins

The French and Indian War wracked the American colonies from 1754 to 1760. France, with many Native American allies, fought England for control of the continent. England won. The Treaty of Paris formally ended the war in 1763. Half the continent changed hands. England was securely in control of almost all of North America, including Canada.

American colonists were delighted. The frontiers now seemed safe. British troops had done most of the fighting, and the British treasury had paid most of the costs. But what seemed like blessings to the colonists soon turned to burdens.

No longer distracted by fighting a powerful enemy, England turned its attention to colonial affairs. The war had been expensive, so England had a large national debt to pay off. England's new, vastly larger North American empire would be vastly more expensive to administer. Clearly, English politicians felt, the colonies should help pay those expenses. So, the British government began a series of attempts to control the colonies and get money from them—a series that led to revolution.

1761 Writs of Assistance

General search warrants in Massachusetts to search for smuggled goods, collect tax.

Proclamation of 1763

Closes western frontier to colonists; saves money, prevents Indian trouble.

1764 Sugar Act

Tariffs on sugar, other items imported into colonies. Other trade laws are enforced.

1765 Stamp Act

Tax stamps on all kinds of printed material.

1765 Quartering Act

Colonials must house and feed British troops in America.

Colonial Protests

Colonists objected to the Writs of Assistance. Smuggling to evade taxes on imports was a way of life in New England port towns. The Proclamation of 1763 angered colonists who itched to move into the bountiful lands west of the Appalachian Mountains. The Sugar Act and other taxes and restrictions on trade caused protests. Colonists also saw no reason for British soldiers to be stationed in a land at peace.

The Stamp Act outraged colonists. It was a direct tax. What right did Parliament have to tax colonies that had no representation in the House of Commons? Mobs rioted, destroying stamps, and the homes of stamp masters. Colonists refused to use the stamps.

Opposition brought the colonists together. The colonies met in a Stamp Act Congress. The radical Sons of Liberty began organized protests. Americans stopped buying British goods. Parliament, urged on by London merchants, gave in and repealed the Stamp Act.

(continued)

Even though their policies were causing colonial rebellion, the British politicians pressed on. They didn't understand Americans. They thought colonials were inferior and needed to be ruled by their betters. So King George III and his ministers had more laws passed:

1766 Declaratory Act
England can make any law it wishes for the colonies.

1767 Townshend Acts
Many new duties on imported goods.

1767 Customs Courts
Trade laws enforced by trial without jury.

Violence Breaks Out

Dissent spread. England was trampling on their "rights of Englishmen," and the colonists objected. Scuffles and brawls increased between residents of New York and Boston and the British troops stationed there. In March 1770, an unruly Boston crowd threw snowballs at British soldiers, who fired and killed five Americans. But things cooled down after this "Boston Massacre" when Parliament repealed the Townshend Acts—except for the tax on tea.

Samuel Adams and other radical Patriots formed "committees of correspondence" and began planning organized intercolony resistance. In November 1773, to protest the tea tax, a group of patriots dressed as Indians destroyed boatloads of British tea in Boston Harbor. Parliament's response was the Coercive Acts, which the colonists called the Intolerable Acts. Among other things, the acts

- Closed Boston Harbor until citizens paid for the dumped tea;
- Severely cut back on Massachusetts self-government.

Resistance Becomes Revolution

Great Britain had made a big mistake. It thought of each colony as a separate unit. But now the colonies united in defense of Massachusetts. The colonies

- Met at the first Continental Congress in Philadelphia in 1774;
- Sent a list of grievances to Parliament;
- Organized a boycott of all British trade in the colonies.

Minutemen—local citizens—began drilling with their militia units throughout Massachusetts and elsewhere.

It all came to a head in April 1775. Parliament responded to the colonists' grievances by declaring that Massachusetts was in a state  of rebellion. British troops marched out of Boston toward the town of Concord to seize ammunition supplies stored there. Patriots Paul Revere and William Dawes rode ahead of the soldiers, rousing the minutemen all along the route. When the British redcoats and the colonial militia faced each other on the green at Lexington, shooting began. In a moment, eight Americans lay dead. Later that day, American militiamen struck back, killing scores of British soldiers as they marched back to Boston.

With these killings, the American Revolution had begun. Still, not all colonials favored independence from Great Britain. Thomas Paine's pamphlet *Common Sense*, published in January 1776, pushed a lot of people into the split-with-England column.

(continued)

*Focus on U.S. History:
The Era of Revolution and Nation-Forming*

The colonists met again at the Second Continental Congress in Philadelphia, in May 1775. On July 2, 1776, they voted:

> "…all political connection between them [the colonies] and the state of Great Britain is, and ought to be, totally dissolved."

On July 4, 1776, the delegates adopted the Declaration of Independence, written by Thomas Jefferson. Then, as now, the Declaration is a great statement of the right to rebel against unjust government and to secure the rights of "life, liberty, and the pursuit of happiness."

Paul Revere's engraving of the Boston Massacre, as seen through Patriot eyes

The Peace of Paris

Directions: The Treaty of Paris formally ended the French and Indian War in 1763. The terms of peace radically changed the colonial power picture. The first group of boxes below shows which colonial powers controlled different areas of America when the war started. Fill in the blanks in the second set of boxes to show how control of these areas changed after the French and Indian War ended.

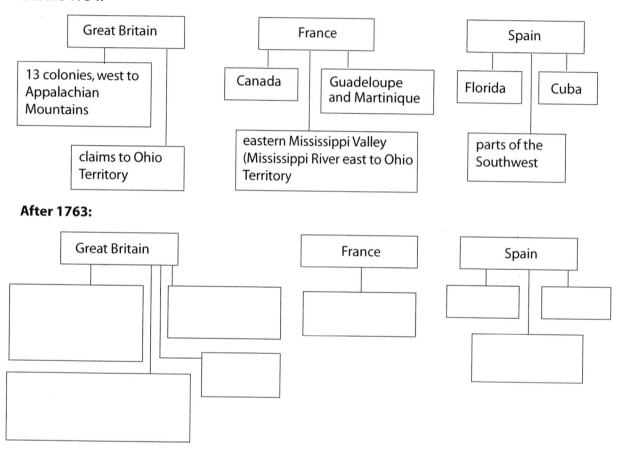

Challenge Question: What was the major result of the war for the American colonies?

Extra Challenge: Show visually how the territory changed hands. Use two copies of your map of eastern North America (page *x*). On the first, use different colors to show territory claimed by England, France, and Spain before the French and Indian War. On the second map, show the territories claimed after the Peace of Paris in 1763. Do the two maps look very different?

Steps to Revolution

Directions: Here is a list of important factors that helped lead up to the American Revolution. Number them in the order in which they occurred in time—1 for the first, 2 for the second, and so on. Then write the highlighted letter of each item in the blank with that item's number. When you're finished, you'll have spelled out a word related to the American Revolution.

_____ The Stamp Act and QuarterinG Acts are passed.

_____ Massachusetts assembly sends out Circular LetteR.

_____ TEa Act is passed, resulting in Boston Tea Party.

_____ ProclamatioN of 1763 is issued.

_____ TownsHend Acts are passed.

_____ Colonists and British troops confront at LexinGton.

_____ BostoN Massacre occurs.

_____ Stamp Act is repealed; DEclaratory Act is passed.

_____ Sugar Act and Currency Acts are passed.

_____ Townshend Acts are repealed.

_____ Intolerable (Coercion) Acts are passed.

_____ Colonials burn *Gaspee*.

_____ Stamp Act Congress meets.

_____ Writs of assistance are authorized.

_____ First COntinental Congress meets.

_____ COmmittees of Correspondence are formed.

Colonists tarring and feathering a colonial tax official

Answer:

__ __ __ __ __ __   __ __ __ __ __ __ __ __ __ __

11 6 15 8 4 13   1 3 5 7 14 9 16 10 12 2

Time Line: Add dates to the items above. Use these, plus other significant items, to construct a time line of events leading to the outbreak of war. Include a brief description of each event. Illustrations would make your time line more interesting.

Voices of Dissent

The colonists had a number of complaints about British policy. Here are some of them.

James Otis, Boston lawyer (1761)

[This writ] seems to me the worst instrument of arbitrary power, the most destructive of English liberty and the fundamental principles of law, that ever was found in an English law-book. . . . Now one of the most essential branches of English liberty is the freedom of one's house. A man's house is his castle. . . . This writ, if it should be declared legal, would totally annihilate this privilege. Custom-house officers may enter our houses, when they please; we are commanded to permit their entry.

The Second Continental Congress (1775)

By one statute it is declared that Parliament can "of right make laws to bind us *in all cases whatsoever*." What is to defend us against so enormous, so unlimited a power? Not a single man of those who assume it is chosen by us; or is subject to our control or influence; but on the contrary, they are all of them exempt from the operation of such laws.

Samuel Adams, radical Patriot (1771)

Is it a time for us to sleep when our free government is essentially changed, and a new one is forming upon a quite different system? A government without the least dependence on the people—a government under the absolute control of a minister of state, upon whose sovereign dictates is to depend . . . [not only] when and . . . where the legislative assembly shall sit, but [also] whether it shall sit at all; and if it is allowed to meet, it shall be liable immediately to be thrown out of existence, if in any one point it fails in obedience to his arbitrary mandates.

John Adams, Patriot (1775)

America has all along consented, still consents, and ever will consent that Parliament, being the most powerful legislature in the dominions, should regulate the trade of the dominions. This is founding the authority of Parliament to regulate our trade upon *compact* and *consent* of the colonies, not upon any principle of common or statute law.

I contend that our provincial legislatures are the only supreme authorities in our colonies. Parliament, notwithstanding this, may be allowed as authority supreme and sovereign over the ocean.

(continued)

Focus on U.S. History:
The Era of Revolution and Nation-Forming

Voices of Dissent *(continued)*

Thomas Fitch, Connecticut governor (1764)

By the constitution, government, and laws of Great Britain, the English are a free people. Their freedom consists principally if not wholly in this general privilege, that "No laws can be made or abrogated without their consent by their representatives in Parliament.". . . No tax . . . can be imposed on them but with their own consent by their representatives in Parliament. . . . It is a clear point that the colonies may not, they cannot, be represented in Parliament.

Stamp Act Congress (1765)

3d. That it is inseparably essential to the freedom of a people, and the undoubted rights of Englishmen, that no taxes should be imposed on them, but with their own consent, given personally, or by their representatives. 4th. That the people of these colonies are not, and from their local circumstances, cannot be, represented in the house of commons in Great Britain. 5th. That the only representatives of the people of these colonies are persons chosen therein, by themselves; and that no taxes ever have been or can be constitutionally imposed on them, but by their respective legislatures.

James Otis, Boston lawyer (1764)

Every British subject born on the continent of America or in any other of the British dominions is by the law of God and nature, by the common law, and by act of Parliament . . . entitled to all the natural, essential, inherent, and inseparable rights of our fellow subjects in Great Britain. . . . The supreme power cannot take from any man any part of his property without his consent in person or by representation. . . .

Now: can there be any liberty where property is taken away without consent? . . . I can see no reason to doubt but that the imposition of taxes, whether on trade, or on land, or houses, or ships, on real or personal, fixed or floating property, in the colonies is absolutely irreconcilable with the rights of the colonists as British subjects and as men. I say men, for in a state of nature no man can take my property from me without my consent.

Directions: From what you have read, in paragraph or outline form summarize the colonists' main objections to British policies and reasons why they objected.

Voices of Consent

Not all colonists objected to British policies. Also, British statesmen justified the mother country's actions toward the colonies. Read these views.

Thomas Hutchinson, chief justice and governor of Massachusetts (1768)

I never think of the measures necessary for the peace and good order of the colonies without pain. There must be an abridgment of what are called English liberties.... I doubt whether it is possible to project a system of government in which a colony 3,000 miles distant from the parent state shall enjoy all the liberty of the parent state.... I wish the good of the colony when I wish to see some further restraint of liberty rather than [that] the connection with the parent state should be broken; for I am sure such a breach must prove the ruin of the colony.

Doctor Samuel Johnson, English writer and thinker (1775)

When they [the colonists] tell of laws made expressly for their punishment, we answer, that tumults and sedition were always punishable, and that the new law prescribes only the mode of execution.... If they are condemned unheard, it is because there is no need of a trial. The crime is manifest and notorious.... If their assemblies have been suddenly dissolved, what was the reason? Their deliberations were indecent, and their intentions seditious. The power of dissolution is granted and reserved for such times of turbulence.... That the same vengeance involves the innocent and guilty is an evil to be lamented, but human caution cannot prevent it, nor human power always redress it. To bring misery on those who have not deserved it is part of the aggregated guilt of rebellion.

Daniel Leonard, Massachusetts lawyer (1775)

Two supreme or independent authorities cannot exist in the same state.... If, then, we are a part of the British Empire, we must be subject to the supreme power of the state, which is vested in the estates of Parliament, notwithstanding each of the colonies have legislative and executive powers of their own, delegated or granted to them for the purposes of regulating their own internal police, which are subordinate to, and must necessarily be subject to, the checks, control, and regulation of the supreme authority.

Were it possible for the colonies to have an equal representation in Parliament, and were [they] refused it upon proper application, I confess I should think it a grievance; but at present it seems to be allowed by all parties to be impracticable, considering the colonies are distant from Great Britain a thousand transmarine leagues.

(continued)

Voices of Consent *(continued)*

William Pitt, Prime Minister of Great Britain (1766)

Upon the whole, I will beg leave to tell the House what is really my opinion. It is, that the Stamp Act be repealed absolutely, totally, and immediately.... At the same time, let the sovereign authority of this country over the colonies be asserted in as strong terms as can be devised, and be made to extend to every point of legislation whatsoever. That we may bind their trade, confine their manufactures, and exercise every power whatsoever, except that of taking their money out of their pockets without their consent.

Samuel Seabury, Tory bishop (1774)

The power, or right, of the British Parliament to raise such a revenue as is necessary for the defense and support of the British government in all parts of the British dominions is therefore incontestable. For, if no government can subsist without a power to raise the revenues necessary for its support, then, in fact, no government can extend any further than its power of raising such a revenue extends. If, therefore, the British Parliament has no power to raise a revenue in the colonies, it has no government over the colonies, *i.e.*, no government that can support itself.... Those that share in the protection of any government are in reason and duty bound to maintain and support the government that protects them....

Our assemblies, from the very nature of things, can have but a ... subordinate and local authority of legislation.... Everything that relates to the internal policy and government of the province which they represent comes properly before them, whether they be matters of law or revenue. But all laws relative to the Empire in general, or to all the colonies conjunctively, or which regulate the trade of any particular colony, in order to make it compatible with the general good of the whole Empire, must be left to the Parliament.

Directions: From what you have read, in paragraph or outline form summarize the main points made by those who supported British policy toward the colonies and how they justified rejecting colonists' complaints.

King George III had no sympathy for the colonists' complaints. Here's what he wrote to Lord North, his prime minister, after the war began (1777):

"No one that reads [Lord Chatham's motion in Parliament], if unacquainted with the conduct of the mother country and its colonies, [but] must suppose the Americans poor mild persons, who after unheard-of and repeated grievances had no choice but slavery or the sword; while the truth is, that the too great leniency of this country increased their pride and encouraged them to rebel."

Loyalist or Patriot?

In the years leading up to the American Revolution, people who thought the colonies should remain tied to England were called **Loyalists**. They were *loyal* to the king. People who wanted the colonies to split from England were called **Patriots**. Which side will you choose? Where you live and what you do for a living could affect your decision. You might also choose sides based on what you really think is right and best.

Directions: Imagine you are each of the following people. Will you choose the Patriot or the Loyalist side? Explain your reasons.

1. You are a newspaper editor and publisher in New York.

2. You are a customs official in Rhode Island.

3. You run a large indigo plantation in South Carolina.

4. You are a sail maker in New Bedford.

5. You are a housewife in Boston.

6. You are a clergyman in Virginia.

7. You are an attorney in Boston.

8. You are a settler on the western frontier of Pennsylvania.

Colonists tarring and feathering a colonial tax official

Extra Challenge: Choose to be one of the people above, or some other equally specific colonial role. With classmates, representing a good mix of Patriots and Loyalists, role-play a debate about splitting away from Great Britain. You can use your outlines and the readings from the *Voices* activities for background.

Focus on U.S. History:
The Era of Revolution and Nation-Forming

Name ______________________________

Date ______________________________

UNIT 1
WORKSHEET 6

One Event, Two Pairs of Eyes

Directions: You probably would have viewed events of the Revolutionary War quite differently depending on whether you were a Patriot or a Loyalist. Try out different points of view: Describe each event below from the Patriot, then from the Loyalist, viewpoint.

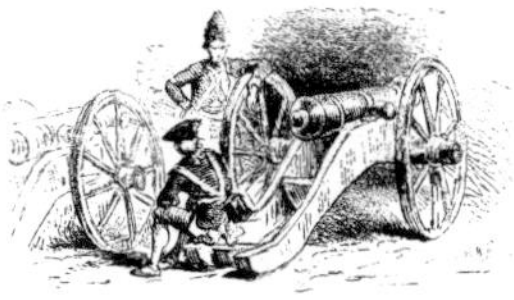

1. **The Boston Massacre**

   Patriot: ______________________________

   ____

   Loyalist: ______________________________

   ____

2. **The Boston Tea Party**

   Patriot: ______________________________

   ____

   Loyalist: ______________________________

   ____

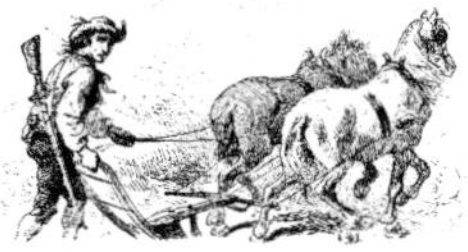

3. **The imposition of the Intolerable Acts**

   Patriot: ______________________________

   ____

   Loyalist: ______________________________

   ____

4. **The fighting at Lexington and Concord**

   Patriot: ______________________________

   ____

   Loyalist: ______________________________

   ____

Two Patriots

Not all Patriots wanted the colonies to declare their independence from Great Britain. Some, led by the radicals, did. Here are two views.

———◆━━━◆━━━◆———

Thomas Paine, radical Patriot (1776)

America would have flourished as much, and probably much more, had no European power taken any notice of her. The commerce by which she has enriched herself are the necessities of life, and will always have a market while eating is the custom of Europe....

We have boasted the protection of Great Britain without considering that her motive was interest, not attachment; and that she did not protect us from our enemies on our account, but from her enemies on her own account, from those who had no quarrel with us on any other account, and who will always be our enemies on the same account....

But Britain is the parent country, say some. Then the more shame upon her conduct. Even brutes do not devour their young, nor savages make war upon their families....

Thomas Paine

Any submission to or dependence on Great Britain tends directly to involve this continent in European wars and quarrels, and sets us at variance with nations who would otherwise seek our friendship, and against whom we have neither anger nor complaint.... Europe is too thickly planted with kingdoms to be long at peace, and whenever a war breaks out between England and any foreign power, the trade of America goes to ruin, because of her connection with Britain....

As to government matters, it is not in the power of Britain to do this continent justice: the business of it will soon be too weighty and intricate to be managed with any tolerable degree of convenience, by a power so distant from us, and so very ignorant of us; for if they cannot conquer us they cannot govern us. To be always running three or four thousand miles with a tale or a petition, waiting four or five months for an answer, which, when obtained, requires five or six more to explain it in, will in a few years be looked upon as folly and childishness. There was a time when it was proper, and there is a proper time for it to cease.

Small islands not capable of protecting themselves are the proper objects for government to take under their care; but there is something absurd in supposing a continent to be perpetually governed by an island....

Everything that is right and reasonable pleads for separation. The blood of the slain, the weeping voice of nature cries, 'TIS TIME TO PART.'...O ye that love mankind! Ye that dare oppose not only the tyranny but the tyrant, stand forth!

———◆━━━◆━━━◆———

(continued)

14

Focus on U.S. History:
The Era of Revolution and Nation-Forming

Two Patriots *(continued)*

———————◆●◆●◆———————

John Dickinson, Pennsylvania lawyer and leading moderate Patriot (1768)

Every government, at some time or other, falls into wrong measures: these may proceed from mistake or passion.—But every such measure does not dissolve the obligation between the governors and the governed; the mistake may be corrected; the passion may pass over....

But if once we are separated from our mother country, what new form of government shall we accept, or when shall we find another Britain to supply our loss? Torn from the body to which we are united by religion, liberty, laws, affections, relations, language, and commerce, we must bleed at every vein....

The constitutional modes of obtaining relief are those which I would wish to see pursued on the present occasion, that is, by petitioning of our assemblies, or, where they are not permitted to meet, of the people to the powers that can afford us relief.

We have an excellent prince, in whose good dispositions towards us we may confide. We have a generous, sensible, and humane nation, to whom

John Dickinson

we may apply. They may be deceived: they may, by artful men, be provoked to anger against us; but I cannot yet believe they will be cruel or unjust; or that their anger will be implacable. Let us behave like dutiful children, who have received unmerited blows from a beloved parent. Let us complain to our parents; but let our complaints speak at the same time, the language of affection and veneration.

———————◆●◆●◆———————

Directions: You are going to use what you've just read to take part in a class debate on the question of whether or not the American colonies should declare themselves independent from Great Britain.

- Decide which side you're going to argue.
- Get together with classmates who are arguing your side also.
- Take notes on the points made for that side by Paine or by Dickinson.
- Develop counterarguments to the points made by Dickinson or Paine for the other side.
- To bolster your side, you could read what other Revolutionary-era Americans wrote to argue these points.
- Debate (or discuss) as a colonial American, not as your present-day self.

Focus on U.S. History:
The Era of Revolution and Nation-Forming

Understanding the Declaration of Independence

Directions: Just what exactly does the Declaration of Independence declare? Complete this exercise to boost your understanding of the Declaration. As a member of a small group, you will develop an explanation of the meaning of one or more of the following phrases from the Declaration of Independence. (Note that reasonable people don't all agree on some of the meanings.) When you're finished, all groups will share their explanations.

"all men"

"are created equal"

"endowed by their Creator"

"unalienable rights"

"the laws of Nature and of Nature's God"

"the pursuit of happiness"

"just powers"

"consent of the governed"

"destructive of these ends"

"abuses and usurpations"

"absolute Despotism"

"absolved from all allegiance"

Extra Challenge: Rewrite this statement from the Declaration of Independence in simpler language:

But when a long train of abuses and usurpations, pursuing invariably the same object, evinces a design to reduce them under absolute despotism, it is their right, it is their duty, to throw off such government.

16

Focus on U.S. History:
The Era of Revolution and Nation-Forming

Why Independence?

Directions: The Declaration of Independence lists the "repeated injuries and usurpations" inflicted on the colonies by the king of England. Tell specifically what each grievance listed below from the Declaration of Independence refers to.

1. He has dissolved representative houses repeatedly, for opposing with manly firmness his invasions on the rights of the people.

   Event: _____

   _____

2. He has kept among us, in times of peace, standing armies without the consent of our legislature.

   Event: _____

   _____

3. He has combined with others to subject us to a jurisdiction foreign to our constitution, and unacknowledged by our laws; giving his assent to their acts of pretended legislation:

   (a) For quartering large bodies of armed troops among us.

      Event: _____

      _____

   (b) For protecting them, by a mock trial, from punishment for any murders which they should commit on the inhabitants of these states.

      Event: _____

      _____

   (c) For cutting off our trade with all parts of the world.

      Event: _____

      _____

   (d) For depriving us in many cases of the benefits of trial by jury.

      Event: _____

      _____

(continued)

Why Independence? *(continued)*

(e) For transporting us beyond seas to be tried for pretended offenses.

Event: _____

_____

(f) For taking away our charters, abolishing our most valuable laws, and altering fundamentally the forms of our governments.

Event: _____

_____

(g) For suspending our own legislature, and declaring themselves invested with power to legislate for us in all cases whatsoever.

Event: _____

_____

4. He has plundered our seas, ravaged our coasts, burned our towns, and destroyed the lives of our people.

Event: _____

_____

5. He is at this time transporting large armies of foreign mercenaries to complete the works of death, desolation, and tyranny, already begun.

Event: _____

_____

6. He has constrained our fellow citizens taken captive on the high seas to bear arms against their country, to become the executioners of their friends and brethren, or to fall themselves by their hands.

Event: _____

_____

7. He has excited domestic insurrections amongst us and has endeavored to bring on the inhabitants of our frontiers the merciless Indian Savages, whose known rule of warfare is an undistinguished destruction of all ages, sexes, and conditions.

Event: _____

_____

Slavery and the Declaration of Independence

Thomas Jefferson's first draft of the Declaration of Independence included a grievance against the king of England for allowing slavery and the slave trade in the colonies. Here's what Jefferson wrote.

> He [the king] has waged cruel war against human nature itself, violating its most sacred rights of life and liberty in the persons of a distant people, who never offended him, captivating and carrying them into slavery in another hemisphere, or to incur miserable death in their transportation thither. This piratical warfare, the opprobrium of infidel powers, is the warfare of the Christian king of Great Britain determined to keep open a market where men should be bought and sold, and he has prostituted his negative for suppressing every legislative attempt to prohibit or to restrain this execrable commerce, determining to keep open a market where men should be bought and sold: and that this assemblage of horrors might want no fact of distinguished dye, he is now exciting those very people to rise in arms among us, and to purchase that liberty of which he has deprived them, by murdering the people upon whom he also obtruded them: thus paying off former crimes committed against the liberties of one people, with crimes which he urges them to commit against the lives of another.

Directions: This is hard to read! Individually or as a member of a small group, explain what each phrase below means or refers to.

1. waged cruel war against human nature: _____

   _____

2. the persons of a distant people: _____

3. in another hemisphere: _____

4. to incur miserable death in their transportation thither: _____

   _____

5. this piratical warfare: _____

   _____

6. the opprobrium of infidel powers: _____

   _____

7. he has prostituted his negative for suppressing every legislative attempt to prohibit:

   _____

   _____

(continued)

Slavery and the Declaration of Independence *(continued)*

8. this execrable commerce: _____

9. that this assemblage of horrors might want no fact of distinguished dye:

   _____

   _____

10. he is now exciting those very people to rise in arms among us: _____

    _____

11. to purchase that liberty of which he has deprived them: _____

    _____

12. the people upon whom he also obtruded them: _____

    _____

13. former crimes committed: _____

    _____

14. crimes which he urges them to commit against the lives of another: _____

    _____

Challenge Question: Jefferson dropped his condemnation of slavery and the slave trade from the final version of the Declaration of Independence.

Slave auction

"The clause reprobating [condemning] the enslaving [of] the inhabitants of Africa was struck out in complaisance [courtesy] to South Carolina and Georgia, who had never attempted to restrain the importation of slaves, and who, on the contrary, still wished to continue it. Our Northern brethren also, I believe, felt a little tender under those censures; for, though their people had very few slaves themselves, yet they had been pretty considerable carriers of them to others."

What two reasons does he give here for dropping the slavery paragraph?

Focus on U.S. History:
The Era of Revolution and Nation-Forming

Fighting the War

The objective of this unit is to help students understand the critical factors that affected the course of the Revolutionary War and the reasons for the American victory. At first glance, a motley group of citizen-soldiers would seem to have little hope of defeating the forces of a mighty empire. But Americans had many advantages on their side, including fighting on their home ground and fighting for a cause. The inexperienced Americans lost important battles at first, but led by George Washington, they learned quickly. The great American victory at Saratoga in 1777 was a turning point in the war because it brought France in on the American side. Other European powers and individuals helped as well. The Revolutionary War affected everyone in the former colonies, not just soldiers. Women, blacks, and Native Americans were all players, on both sides. When the war ended, the political map of North America had once again changed greatly. This unit's activities will draw students into a better understanding of these aspects of the American Revolution.

Student Activities

The War: Time Line and Mapping strengthens students' knowledge of the chronology and major events of the war. They identify the date and month of specific events, write brief descriptions of each, and then construct a time line, or add to the time line they started in Unit 1.

In **Battle Results** students assume the perspectives of different Revolutionary War military leaders. Students explain why a hypothetical statement made by each of the five leaders about a battle's outcome is or is not accurate. For an extra challenge students can role-play a military tribunal investigating the conduct of a Revolutionary War battle.

A Failed Plan uses mapping to demonstrate how battle plans often don't work in the field as they were intended to on paper, asking students to trace the planned and actual course of the British campaign in New York State.

The Stars and Stripes traces the evolution of the American flag during the 1700's. The Extra Challenge gives artistically inclined students a chance to do some research and create a colorful poster of Revolutionary-era flags.

A Soldier's Life uses original-source readings to present a vivid picture of the miseries of life for a Revolutionary War soldier. Students list hardships soldiers endured that are evident in the readings. For an extra challenge they can debate whether soldiers living in horrible conditions, as at Valley Forge, had the right to leave and go home to their families.

In **The Opposing Armies**, students identify military advantages and disadvantages for each side and list factors that counterbalanced British strategic superiorities.

Who Said It? presents memorable sayings from the American Revolution and asks students to identify the speakers. As an extra challenge, students can become more familiar with these people by identifying the occasion of each quote.

Civilians in Wartime uses original-source readings to give students snapshots of civilian life during the Revolutionary War. After doing more reading—diaries, letters, testimony, historical fiction—students describe how particular wartime circumstances affected civilians.

Europeans and the American Army gives thumbnail sketches of Europeans who made important contributions to the American Revolution. Students do research on one of these people and then give a speech to the class, in character, about that person's life and contributions.

The Allies guides students through a series of questions to identify the roles that Spain, France, and Holland played in the American Revolution.

Mapping the Peace uses mapping to show how the 1783 Treaty of Paris once again changed the political map of North America and how the alliance system operated during the war. For an extra challenge students amplify the map to include western land claims by eastern states.

The War Ends: Another Treaty of Paris uses a chart to compare how territory lost or gained with the 1783 Treaty of Paris affected the economic and strategic interests of the United States, Native American nations, France, Spain, and Great Britain.

Fighting the War

Americans Versus British

At first glance, the colonists' chances of winning the war looked hopeless. They were an informal collection of farmers, merchants, artisans, and other civilians. Their weapons were mostly whatever they kept at home for hunting. They hated military discipline. Their country was mostly agricultural. It didn't manufacture the tools of war, and it didn't have the money to pay for a war. It didn't even have a national government or a national army!

Against this band of rebels was arrayed a mighty empire. England ruled the seas. It was industrial, so it could make plenty of war materials. It had a large population to draw on for its army. Its government was strong and centralized. Its soldiers were highly trained and experienced.

Yet, the Americans won. How did this happen? Factors that weren't at first obvious came into play. Britain had to send fresh supplies and men to its army from a base thousands of miles across the sea. Americans were fighting on their home turf; more men and supplies could always be found when needed. British soldiers fought for pay or instead of serving a jail sentence. Americans were fighting for their homes, their families, their land, their rights, and their freedom. Gradually they became a disciplined and determined military force. The British Army was inefficient and poorly directed. The colonists had a common cause and a leader—George Washington—to unite them.

War in the North

In 1775 the bloody British retreat from Concord and the American valor at Bunker Hill showed that colonial soldiers could and would fight well. Then General Howe easily defeated the inexperienced Washington at the Battle of Long Island in August 1776. Washington was a fast learner, though. He won victories at Trenton and Princeton the following December and January. The British developed a grand plan to control the Hudson River, but they didn't carry it out right, and the Americans won a great victory at Saratoga in the fall of 1777.

But aside from that, the war went mostly England's way for a while.

- British troops defeated colonials at Brandywine and Germantown.
- General Howe occupied Philadelphia for the winter.
- Washington's troops endured cold and hunger at Valley Forge.

Valley Forge

France Steps in

The victory at Saratoga did change things, though. France had been helping the colonies with supplies and munitions, since Britain was also an enemy of France. Benjamin Franklin and his colleagues were in Paris to encourage this. News of Saratoga convinced France to sign a formal treaty of alliance with the colonies early in 1778. French troops and officers landed

(continued)

Focus on U.S. History:
The Era of Revolution and Nation-Forming

in America, and ships from the French Navy challenged British control of offshore waters.

While the war raged, civilians suffered. Colonists who remained loyal to King George, or Loyalists, lost their homes, their businesses, and their money. Many had to leave the colonies. Families split between Loyalists and Patriots. Goods normally imported from abroad were scarce. Food and farm animals became supplies for the army. Money lost a lot of its value, and the price of everything skyrocketed. Currency issued by the Continental Congress was worth almost nothing—"not worth a Continental," as we sometimes still say.

War in the South

The war moved south in 1778. British troops took over most of Georgia in 1778 and 1779. They occupied Charleston and other parts of South Carolina in 1780. They thought pro-English sentiment in the South would keep them in control. But the South had plenty of Patriots too. Colonial forces led by Francis Marion (the "Swamp Fox") and Nathanael

Greene kept raiding and harassing the British troops, who finally withdrew to North Carolina.

Victory and Peace

In 1781 the British general Cornwallis established a base at Yorktown, in Virginia. Washington's colonial army and Rochambeau's French troops trapped Cornwallis there. The French admiral de Grasse and his fleet fought off the British Navy and blockaded the rivers leading to Yorktown. Cornwallis couldn't escape by land or by sea. He surrendered, and the war was over.

After the surrender at Yorktown, the Congress sent a group of very able men to Paris to discuss peace terms. The group included John Adams (who became the second U.S. president), Thomas Jefferson (who was the third president), John Jay, and Benjamin Franklin. They negotiated a very good deal: England gave up all of North America south of Canada and west to the Mississippi River, except for Spanish Florida.

Washington commanding the troops

The War: Time Line and Mapping

Directions: Write the month and year when it occurred next to each major event of the Revolutionary War listed below. Then construct a time line of these and any other events you think are significant. (Or, add these events to the time line you started in Unit 1.) Include a brief description of each event. Illustrations would enhance your time line.

1. **Battle of Lexington and Concord**   Date: _____

   Brief description: _____

2. **Capture of Fort Ticonderoga**   Date: _____

   Brief description: _____

3. **American defeat at Quebec**   Date: _____

   Brief description: _____

4. **Second Continental Congress meets**   Date: _____

   Brief description: _____

5. **Battle of Bunker Hill**   Date: _____

   Brief description: _____

6. **George Washington named commander-in-chief**   Date: _____

   Brief description: _____

7. **Battle of Trenton**   Date: _____

   Brief description: _____

8. **British evacuate Boston**   Date: _____

   Brief description: _____

9. **Battle of Long Island**   Date: _____

   Brief description: _____

10. **Declaration of Independence issued**   Date: _____

    Brief description: _____

11. **British occupy New York City**   Date: _____

    Brief description: _____

(continued)

The War: Time Line and Mapping *(continued)*

12. **Battle of Saratoga**   Date: _____

   Brief description: _____

13. **British occupy Philadelphia**   Date: _____

   Brief description: _____

14. **Articles of Confederation adopted**   Date: _____

   Brief description: _____

15. **Battle of Brandywine**   Date: _____

   Brief description: _____

16. **Winter at Valley Forge**   Date: _____

   Brief description: _____

17. **Battle of Monmouth Court House**   Date: _____

   Brief description: _____

18. **Fall of Savannah**   Date: _____

   Brief description: _____

19. **Alliance with France**   Date: _____

   Brief description: _____

Washington crossing the Delaware

(continued)

Focus on U.S. History:
The Era of Revolution and Nation-Forming

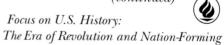

The War: Time Line and Mapping (continued)

20. **Spain enters the war**   Date: _____

    Brief description: _____

21. **Siege of Charleston**   Date: _____

    Brief description: _____

22. **Benedict Arnold's treason discovered**   Date: _____

    Brief description: _____

23. **French and British battle in Chesapeake Bay**   Date: _____

    Brief description: _____

24. **Siege of Yorktown**   Date: _____

    Brief description: _____

25. **Cornwallis surrenders**   Date: _____

    Brief description: _____

Cornwallis surrendering

Mapping Directions: On your map of Eastern North America (page *x*), trace the major army movements of the war. (Use two different colors, one for British and one for American forces.) Also locate and label the major battle sites on your map. Use time-line items 1 to 25 as a guide.

Battle Results

Directions: Victory and defeat aren't always clear-cut. Perhaps something was saved in a retreat. Maybe more could have been won. Here are some statements Revolutionary War leaders might have made. Explain how each is or is not accurate.

1. **George Washington:** All things considered, I saved the day at the Battle of Long Island and the fighting in New York City right afterward.

2. **General William Howe:** I got the best possible result when I engaged Washington and his army at Long Island and New York City.

3. **General John Burgoyne:** I did my part in the upstate New York campaign, and I did it well, but I was let down by St. Leger and Howe.

4. **Colonel William Prescott:** In spite of the fact that we lost Bunker Hill and Breed's Hill, the fight was a triumph for American forces.

5. **Lord Charles Cornwallis:** I made a bad mistake by surrendering at Yorktown.

Extra Challenge: Role-play the parts of officers and soldiers taking part in a military tribunal. The tribunal is inquiring into the conduct of a Revolutionary War battle. The purpose is to determine if the commanders of the battle did the best they could under the circumstances. Battles you might consider for this exercise include these: Quebec, the Americans, 1775; Charleston, the British, 1776; Charleston, the Americans, 1780.

28

Focus on U.S. History:
The Era of Revolution and Nation-Forming

Map: Upstate New York and Philadelphia Campaigns

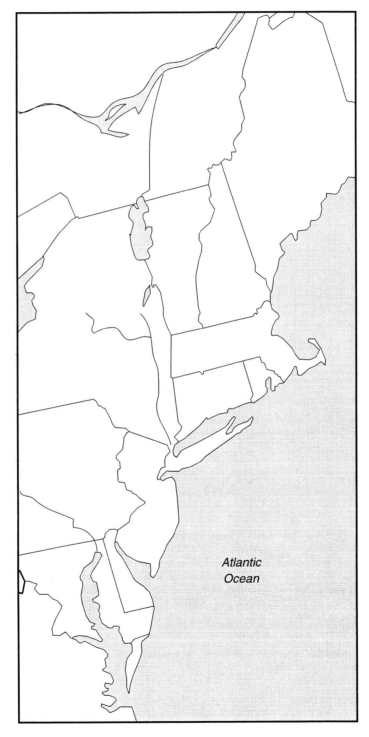

Atlantic
Ocean

*Focus on U.S. History:
The Era of Revolution and Nation-Forming*

A Failed Plan

Directions: The British had a great plan to divide the colonies and win the war. You'll see what it was as you fill in your map of the New York and Philadelphia campaigns (Unit 2, Worksheet 3). Follow these steps.

1. Start by locating and labeling the following features on the map.

Quebec	Princeton	Kingston	St. Lawrence River
Montreal	Trenton	Fort Oswego	Richelieu River
Albany	Germantown	Fort Stanwix	Hudson River
New York City	Brandywine	Crown Point	Mohawk River
Philadelphia	Ticonderoga	Saratoga/Stillwater	Atlantic Ocean
Lake Champlain	Lake George	Lake Ontario	Chesapeake Bay

2. Show how the British plan was supposed to work. Trace these planned routes with dotted lines:

General John Burgoyne

Lieutenant Colonel Barry St. Leger

General William Howe

Question: What would be the main effect of this strategy if it succeeded?

_____

3. Neat plan! But all did not go as planned. On the map, in a solid line, show what actually happened, and where, with dates.

Burgoyne (leaves base, takes fort, surrenders)

St. Leger (leaves first base, leaves second base, fights, retreats)

Howe (leaves base, attacks)

General Sir Henry Clinton (leaves base, proceeds, returns)

4. Also, show the positions and movements of American forces:

General George Washington

General Benedict Arnold and General Horatio Gates

General John Burgoyne

Focus on U.S. History:
The Era of Revolution and Nation-Forming

The Stars and Stripes

Directions: Complete this activity to see how the American flag developed.
Note: The square in the upper left corner of a flag is called the **canton**.

Union Jack

White cross stands for: _____

Red cross stands for: _____

Together they stand for: _____

Date: _____

New England Flag

Pine tree stands for: _____

Red cross stands for: _____

Date: _____

Taunton Flag

Liberty and Union

Canton stands for: _____

Where it flew: _____

Date: _____

Continental Navy Flag

Don't Tread On Me

Stripes stand for: _____

Where it flew: _____

Date: _____

Continental Colors, or Grand Union Flag

Canton stands for: _____

Stripes stand for: _____

Where it flew: _____

Date: _____

Stars and Stripes

Canton stands for: _____

_____

Date: _____

Extra Challenge: Create a full-color poster of these and other flags of the Revolutionary era.

A Soldier's Life

Being a Revolutionary War soldier could be a miserable experience. Read these descriptions.

Doctor Albigence Waldo, describing Valley Forge (1777)

I am sick—discontented—and out of humor. Poor food—hard lodging—cold weather—fatigue—nasty clothes—nasty cookery—vomit half my time—smoked out of my senses—the devil's in't—I can't endure it—Why are we sent here to starve and freeze? …—Here comes a bowl of beef soup—full of burnt leaves and dirt—away with it boys—I'll live like the chameleon upon air.…

See the poor soldier, when in health—with what cheerfulness he meets his foes and encounters every hardship—if barefoot—he labors through the mud and cold with a song in his mouth extolling war and Washington—if his food be bad—he eats it notwithstanding with seeming content.… A moment—There comes a soldier—His bare feet are seen through his worn out shoes—his legs nearly naked from the tattered remains of an only pair of stockings—his breeches not sufficient to cover his nakedness—his shirt hanging in strings—his hair disheveled—his face meager—his whole appearance pictures a person forsaken and discouraged. He comes, and cries with an air of wretchedness and despair—I am sick—my feet lame—my legs are sore—my body covered with this tormenting itch—my clothes are worn out—my constitution is broken—my former activity is exhausted by fatigue—hunger and cold—I fail fast; I shall soon be no more! and all the reward I shall get will be—"Poor Will is dead."…

Yesterday upwards of fifty officers in General Green's division resigned their commissions. All this is occasioned by officers' families being so much neglected at home.… [The officers'] wages [are not enough to] purchase a few trifling comfortables here in camp, and maintain their families at home [also].

James Thatcher, army medic (1780)

Repeated complaints have been made … that some of the soldiers are in the practice of pilfering and plundering the inhabitants of their poultry, sheep, pigs, and even their cattle, from their farms. This marauding practice has often been prohibited.… Death has been inflicted in a few instances of an atrocious nature, but in general, the punishment consists in a public whipping. The law of Moses prescribed forty stripes save one, but this number has often been exceeded in our camp. In aggravated cases, and with old offenders, the culprit is sentenced to receive one hundred lashes, or more.… The culprit being securely tied to a tree, or post, receives on his naked back the number of lashes assigned him, by a whip formed of several small knotted cords, which sometimes cut through the skin at every stroke.

(continued)

32

A Soldier's Life *(continued)*

George Washington, commander-in-chief (1779)

The situation of the army with respect to supplies, is beyond the description alarming. It has been five or six weeks past on half allowance, and we have not more than three days bread, at a third allowance, on hand, nor any where within reach....We have never experienced a like extremity at any period of the war.

Israel Trask, sailor (1782)

On board the *Perseverance* [a prison ship] the prisoners were driven down under the haulup deck, their only beds large ironbound water casks, with a stifled, impure air to respire [breathe]. Only four in the daytime and one at night were allowed to leave this dungeon to catch the pure air or answer the calls of nature. In about a fortnight we were relieved from these impurities to be thrust into a filthy prison ship at Halifax, a large old condemned East Indiaman. On her three decks were housed, or entombed, some hundreds of our countrymen, many of whom had been her occupants for three long years. The gloomy aspect of the ship, the cadaverous appearance of the prisoners, made death preferable to a lengthy abode in this horrific Avernus.

Directions: From what you have read, list here the many hardships Revolutionary War soldiers had to endure.

_____   _____

_____   _____

_____   _____

_____   _____

_____   _____

_____   _____

Extra Challenge: With classmates, debate or discuss this question: Did soldiers living in such dreadful conditions as those at Valley Forge, not being paid or clothed or fed adequately, have a right to desert and go home to their families? (Many did.)

Name _____

Date _____

The Opposing Armies

Part 1 Directions: Here's a list of phrases that describe Revolutionary War soldiers. Your task is to identify whether the soldiers being described are American or British. Then tell whether what the description says is an advantage or a disadvantage for the army that the soldiers belong to.

	American or British?	Advantage or Disadvantage?
1. Well trained, well disciplined		
2. Skilled marksmen		
3. Sign up for short term of service		
4. Carry heavy packs and muskets		
5. Fight for own home, land, country		
6. Convicts, extreme lower class		
7. Use many primitive weapons		
8. Skilled at guerrilla-type warfare		
9. Not professional or well trained		
10. Fight for pay for a foreign country		
11. Skilled in use of bayonet		
12. Fight for a cause		
13. Provide own equipment		
14. Resist discipline, drilling		

Part 2 Directions: The British forces had many advantages over the Americans. But the British advantages, as it turned out, were counterbalanced by disadvantages or by American assets. Identify these counterbalances below.

1. The British were masters of the sea, and the Americans had little or no navy.
   Counterbalance: _____

2. The British had a large industrial base to draw on to supply troops.
   Counterbalance: _____

3. The British had a much greater population to supply soldiers and money to hire more.
   Counterbalance: _____

4. The British had a strong central, national government, and the Americans did not.
   Counterbalance: _____

34   *Focus on U.S. History:*
The Era of Revolution and Nation-Forming

Who Said It?

Directions: The American Revolution was one of the most memorable events in our history, and it produced sayings that we still remember today. Which well-known figure of the Revolutionary era said (or wrote) each of the following quotes?

1. We must indeed all hang together, or most assuredly we will all hang separately.

   Speaker: _____

2. Taxation without representation is tyranny.

   Speaker: _____

3. Stand your ground. Don't fire unless fired upon. But if they mean to have a war, let it begin here.

   Speaker: _____

4. Don't one of you fire until you see the whites of their eyes.

   Speaker: _____

5. Give me liberty, or give me death!

   Speaker: _____

6. Don't give up the ship! **Speaker:** _____

7. These are the times that try men's souls.

   Speaker: _____

8. I only regret that I have but one life to lose for my country.

   Speaker: _____

9. I have not yet begun to fight.

   Speaker: _____

10. There! I guess King George will be able to read that without his glasses.

    Speaker: _____

11. In my opinion, there never was a good war or a bad peace.

    Speaker: _____

12. I desire you would remember the ladies.

    Speaker: _____

Extra Challenge: Identify the occasion on which each quotation above was spoken or written.

Civilians in Wartime

Read the diary entries and testimonies below. They tell you something about life during the war for men, women, and children who weren't soldiers or who served in the army temporarily.

Abigail Adams, writing about Boston (1775)

Their beef is all spent; their malt and cider all gone. All the fresh provisions they can procure, they are obliged to give to the sick and wounded.... No man dared now to be seen talking to his friend in the street. They were obliged to be within, every evening, at ten o'clock, according to martial law....

Every article here in the West India way is very scarce and dear ... not one pin to be purchased for love or money.

Abigail Adams

John Suddarth, age thirteen (1778)

[I] volunteered in the army of the United States about the last of June 1778 [at age thirteen] as a substitute for [my] brother James Suddarth.... [I] was engaged as a private in guarding the prisoners in the county.... [I] continued in this service until the last of September (a period of three months), when [I] was relieved by the return of [my] brother for whom [I] had substituted ... and who had been compelled to leave the service in consequence of sickness.

A resident of Boston, after the British evacuated (1776)

On passing into the town, it presented an indescribable scene of desolation and gloominess.... [O]ur minds were impressed with an awful sadness at the sight of the ruins of many houses which had been taken down for fuel—the dirtiness of the streets—the wretched appearance of the very few inhabitants who remained during the siege.... [W]e entered the Old South church, and had ocular [visual] demonstration that it had been turned into a *riding school*, for the use of General Burgoyne's regiment of cavalry.... The pulpit and all the pews were taken away and burnt for fuel, and many hundred loads of dirt and gravel were carted in, and spread upon the floor. The south door was closed, and a bar was fixed, over which the cavalry were taught to leap their horses at full speed. A grog shop was erected in the gallery.

Reverend Stephen Williams (1776)

31—The last day of the year. It has been one of the most remarkable in the history of America. The people, by their Congress, have declared Independency, and the king's troops and fleets are come against us. Battles have been fought; forts and towns taken; much blood shed; many taken captive and wounded; many sick, and many have died in our army. Sickness has everywhere prevailed; deaths have been many; a day of darkness indeed.

(continued)

Civilians in Wartime *(continued)*

Sarah Osborn, camp follower (1781)

[I] took [my] stand just back of the American tents, say about a mile from the town, and busied [myself] washing, mending, and cooking for the soldiers, in which [I] was assisted by the other females; some men washed their own clothing.... [I] cooked and carried in beef, and bread, and coffee (in a gallon pot) to the soldiers in the entrenchment. On one occasion when [I] was thus employed carrying in provisions, [I] met General Washington, who asked if [I] "was not afraid of the cannonballs?" [I] replied ..."It would not do for the men to fight and starve too."

David Freemoyer, soldier (1780)

The enemy [British soldiers and Indians] set fire to and burned a mill on the Schoharie River.... After this the enemy passed down the Schoharie and then up the Mohawk River, laying waste and destroying everything before them.

Directions: Complete this activity as a member of a small group. Each member of the group will read more diary entries, letters, and testimony from people who lived during the American Revolution. You can also read historical novels set during that time. Then, as a group, describe how these wartime circumstances affected civilians in the following areas.

1. British occupation of cities or towns

2. Civilian involvement with the American Army

3. Shortages of food and goods

4. Taking over responsibilities of men who were serving in the army

5. Physical damages caused by the war

6. Civilian casualties during the war

Europeans and the American Army

Directions: Some individual Europeans gave important—maybe crucial—help to the American Army. You (individually or as a member of a small group) will choose one of the men identified in the thumbnail sketches below. Do some reading about him. Then assume the character of that person and deliver a speech to the class in which you describe your life and your contributions to the American Revolution. Is anything in the United States today named after you?

Baron Friedrich
Wilhelm von Steuben

Marquis de Lafayette: A rich, young French nobleman, just nineteen years old when he volunteered to serve.

Baron Friedrich Wilhelm von Steuben: A Prussian army captain who yelled and swore while drilling American recruits into trained soldiers.

Count Kazimierz Pulaski: A Polish military commander who organized an American cavalry unit and died fighting in Georgia.

Baron Johann de Kalb: A German who became a general in the American Army and died fighting in South Carolina.

Tadeusz Kosciuszko: A Polish general and engineer who later became a freedom fighter in his native country.

Caron de Beaumarchais: A French playwright who used a dummy company to funnel supplies to the American Army.

Comte de Rochambeau: A French army officer who led his French force south to Yorktown with Washington and his troops.

Comte de Grasse: A French admiral who made the victory at Yorktown possible.

The Allies

Directions: The Americans wanted and needed European help in the war. Did they get it? Find out by answering these questions.

1a. Why might France help? _____

_____

1b. What exactly does France want to gain by helping? _____

_____

1c. What did France actually do to help? _____

_____

2a. Why might Spain help? _____

_____

2b. What exactly does Spain want to gain by helping?

_____

_____

2c. What did Spain actually do to help? _____

_____

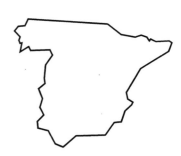

3a. Why might Holland help?_____

_____

3b. What exactly does Holland want to gain by helping?

_____

_____

3c. What did Holland actually do to help? _____

_____

Mapping the Peace

Part 1 Directions: On your map of eastern North America (page x), show the new territorial boundaries established by the 1783 Treaty of Paris. Show the following:

> • Boundaries of the United States
>
>   the thirteen states
>
>   the Northwest Territory (established in 1787)
>
>   other frontier districts
>
> • Spanish territories
>
> • British territories

Compare this map with the ones you made for The Peace of Paris in Unit 1.

Extra Challenge: On your map of eastern North America, show which states claimed which parts of the Northwest Territory and the other parts of the eastern Mississippi Valley.

Part 2 Directions: The peace negotiations were complicated because of the alliances. Draw lines below to show which nations were allies of each other. Color all allied nations the same color.

The War Ends: Another Treaty of Paris

Directions: The Treaty of Paris of 1783 formally ended the Revolutionary War. It set down the terms of the peace. On this chart, identify what each nation gained or lost by the treaty.

	Territory Gained/Lost	Effect on Economic Interests	Effect on Strategic Interests
United States			
Native American nations			
France			
Spain			
Great Britain			

Focus on U.S. History:
The Era of Revolution and Nation-Forming

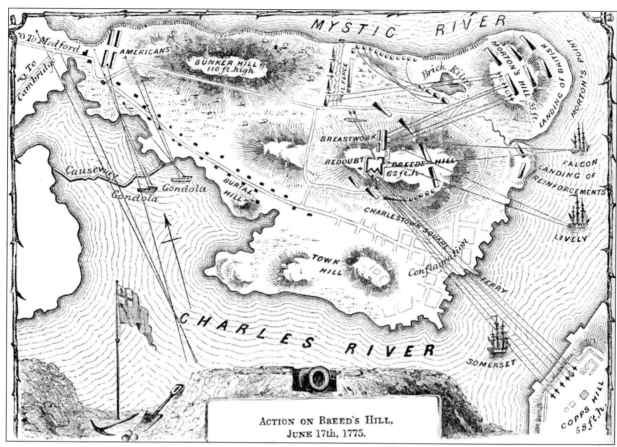

Site of the Battle of Bunker Hill

American troops building a protective barrier on Breed's Hill

Prayer before the battle as the British soldiers approached

Changing American Society

The objectives of this unit are to help students better understand the American Revolution's effects on different social groups and to identify aspects of the new American nationalism. African-Americans, free and slave, fought on both sides during the war. The fight for liberty and independence spurred hopes for the end of slavery, which was, in fact, abolished from many northern states in the years following the Revolution. Free African-Americans worked hard to improve life for their fellows during these times. Native Americans, too, had fought on both sides during the war. But the British defeat was ominous for America's Indians. The American national government was unlikely to be able to restrain the hordes of white settlers hungry for Indian lands. Women had also been active during the war, running businesses and farms and following the arguments for liberty and equality with keen interest. The postwar years saw increased female aspirations and opportunities and stirrings of a movement for widespread female education. Also in the postwar years, the wartime unity and the great victory over the British inspired a new spirit of American nationalism. This unit's activities are designed to draw students into a greater understanding of these aspects and results of the American Revolution.

Student Activities

Native Americans and the Revolutionary Era uses visual, completion, and mapping exercises to familiarize students with the alliances between Native Americans and American or British forces and with major conflicts that involved Indians during the war.

Who Was I? African-American Society provides students with thumbnail sketches of prominent African-Americans of the Revolutionary era. For each, students must answer the question, "Who was I?" The Extra Challenge expands on this activity by having students write a more complete biography of one of these people.

Women in Revolutionary America introduces a number of Revolutionary-era women. Students must match each woman's name with her occupation (which includes unexpected ones, like Indian chief and artilleryman). For an extra challenge students can do research on one of these women and write a biography of her.

The Rights of Women presents original-source readings by and about Revolutionary-era women, commenting on women's status in society and the proper role of education for women at that time. Students find evidence in the readings of revolutionary new ideas about women as well as thinking that holds women back in their traditional limited sphere.

Close-up: Daughters of Liberty presents a contemporary description of American women patriots and a brief biography of a prominent daughter of liberty, Mercy Otis Warren.

In **An American National Spirit** students identify elements of the new national spirit in such areas as architecture, painting, science, and education. Students then use illustrations of those examples to create a "National Spirit" classroom display.

Effects of the Revolution asks students to assume the viewpoint of various Revolutionary-era people to imagine what each individual might have hoped the Revolution would accomplish and what effect the Revolution might actually have had.

American soldiers on patrol in Indian territory during the Revolution

Changing American Society

African-Americans

Successfully fighting a revolution changed American society in many ways. Colonists had fought for freedom. They had declared that "all men are created equal" and had a right to liberty. So, what about slaves? The talk about equality and liberty prompted the new states in the North to do away with slavery. By the mid-1800's, it was gone from there. People hoped this meant it would gradually disappear from the South too. But this didn't happen.

During the war, many blacks had fought on both sides. Lord Dunmore, the royal governor of Virginia, had promised black slaves their freedom if they would fight for the British. Many did fight, but they didn't all get their freedom at the war's end. Others were taken from their masters as "property." These people might be sent to the West Indies as slaves or freed and sent to Canada or Africa. Other slaves simply ran away when the southern countryside was in turmoil.

At first, the Colonial Army tried to ban blacks. Blacks with guns could mean a slave

Richard Allen

uprising. But then Lord Dunmore made his promise, and the Colonial Army needed men. So blacks were allowed to serve after all, and many did. After the war, prominent black leaders like Paul Cuffe, Richard Allen, and Prince Hall continued to work for freedom for all their enslaved people.

Native Americans

Native Americans during the war mostly allied with the British. With good justification they feared the colonists' thirst for the frontier lands—Indian lands—across the Appalachians. Most Indians saw a British victory as their best chance to contain the colonists' westward push. So, the war on the western and northern frontiers saw many raids and counterraids. Terrible things happened. Indians and Loyalists carried out the Wyoming, Pennsylvania, massacre in 1778. In response, the Sullivan expedition in 1778 and 1779 destroyed many peaceful Iroquois villages.

The American victory doomed Indians in the East. Treaties were supposed to protect Native American lands in the Ohio Territory and other frontier areas. The Northwest Ordinance specifically called for dealing with Indians with "utmost good faith." Nevertheless, the tide of settlers would eventually sweep Native Americans off their lands.

Burning a Native American village

(continued)

Women and Their Rights

While the men were off fighting the war, women kept society going. They ran their husband's, father's, or brother's businesses. They ran the farms and plantations. Everyone could see that women were perfectly capable of doing all sorts of things they hadn't been expected to or allowed to do before.

Abigail Adams

Patriotic women began to apply the ideas of liberty and equality to themselves. Abigail Adams even suggested to her husband John that women shouldn't be bound to obey any laws imposed by men whom they couldn't vote to elect. (This was the same argument colonists had used against taxes imposed on them by the British Parliament.)

No one was ready for big changes in a woman's status yet, though. Wives were still ruled by their husbands—they couldn't even own their own property. But for a republic to succeed, its citizens must be educated. Women, therefore, needed decent educations so they could train their children to be responsible citizens. As a result, in the years after the Revolution many new schools for girls were started.

A National Spirit

Revolution often means big social changes. But that didn't happen in the newly independent states. Society did tend to become a bit more equal. Farmers and small shopkeepers were less likely to take second place behind large landowners and wealthy businessmen. Also, all citizens expected politicians and state officials to listen to their opinions and follow their wishes.

Uniting to defeat the British enemy gave Americans a new spirit of nationalism. Before the war people had been focused mostly on their own colony and its way of life. During the war, soldiers experienced life in other colonies. So did the hordes of camp followers. New Englanders and southerners met and lived side-by-side, perhaps for the first time. Leaders from all the colonies traveled the country and met one another in Philadelphia. The colonists who fought together for the same cause were now Americans.

Native Americans and the Revolutionary Era

Part 1 Directions: Some Native American groups fought in the Revolution. Some were allies of the British. Others fought with the Americans. Either way, they ended up losing land. Identify Indian allies of the Americans and the British below. Choose from among these Native American groups:

Catawba—Cayuga—Cherokee—Creek—Delaware—Iroquois—Miami—Mohawk

Oneida—Onondaga—Ottawa—Seneca—Tuscarora

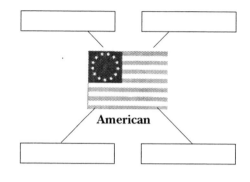

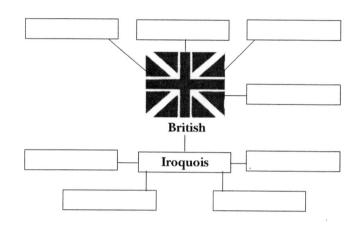

Part 2 Directions: Here are some major Native American conflicts during and just after the Revolutionary War. Fill in the missing information. Locate the items marked with an asterisk (*) on your map of eastern North America.

Lord Dunmore's War, 1774

Native American groups involved:

_____

Native American leaders:

_____

*Site of decisive British victory:

_____

Cherokee raids, 1776–77

*States involved:

_____

Wyoming Valley raids 1778

Native American groups involved:

_____

*Wyoming massacre

*Cherry Valley massacre

Sullivan's expedition, 1778–79

Native Americans involved:

_____

*Indian villages, crops, orchards destroyed

Who Was I? African-American Society

Directions: Identify each of these prominent African-Americans of the Revolutionary era.

I was the first black, the first slave, and the third woman to publish a book of poems in the United States. 1. Who was I? _____	Born free, I became a master mariner and a shipbuilder. I worked tirelessly to help black Americans settle in Sierra Leone in Africa. 2. Who was I? _____	Born a slave, I won my freedom by arguing that the Massachusetts Bill of Rights said I was born free and equal. A court agreed. 3. Who was I? _____
I was a minister originally from Barbados. I founded the first chapter of black Masons in the 1780's. 4. Who was I? _____	I was the first published black American poet, a slave in New York State, and a minister to my people. 5. Who was I? _____	I was at Lexington. Then at Bunker Hill I killed the British major who had been in charge at Lexington. 6. Who was I? _____
A keen astronomer, I became known as the "Black Poor Richard" for my series of almanacs. I helped lay out the streets of the new national capital city. 7. Who was I? _____	I was taken from Africa when I was a young child. I was a poet who lived in Deerfield, Massachusetts, and Vermont. I argued a case before the U.S. Supreme Court. 8. Who was I? _____	I bought my freedom from my master in Delaware and organized the Free African Society in Philadelphia. My church became known as the Bethel African Methodist Episcopal Church. 9. Who was I? _____
I ran away from my master and became a sailor. I led the group against the soldiers and was first to fall at the Boston Massacre. 10. Who was I? _____	Disguised as a man named Robert Shurtliff, I was a female soldier in the Continental Army during the Revolutionary War. 11. Who was I? _____	I was kidnapped into slavery from Nigeria as a child. The *Narrative* I wrote about my life's experiences was widely read. 12. Who was I? _____

*Focus on U.S. History:
The Era of Revolution and Nation-Forming*

Women in Revolutionary America

Directions: Women had many roles in the Revolutionary era. Match each woman's name below with her occupation. (Most of these women were also housewives, which in those days was more than a full-time job in itself.)

_____ 1. Mercy Otis Warren
_____ 2. Phillis Wheatley
_____ 3. Mary Brant
_____ 4. Mary Hays
_____ 5. Elizabeth Flanagan
_____ 6. Abigail Adams
_____ 7. Esther Reed
_____ 8. Eliza Lucas Pinckney
_____ 9. Margaret Corbin
_____ 10. Mary Katherine Goddard
_____ 11. Nancy Ward
_____ 12. Betsy Ross
_____ 13. Deborah Reed Franklin
_____ 14. Flora McDonald
_____ 15. Elizabeth Freeman
_____ 16. Deborah Sampson
_____ 17. Nancy Van Alstyne

a. soldier
b. housewife, printer
c. camp follower, cannoneer
d. Loyalist activist
e. flag maker
f. house servant, former slave
g. Mohawk Indian leader
h. historian, playwright
i. artilleryman
j. poet
k. Indian fighter
l. tavern keeper
m. fundraiser for the army
n. political observer, writer
o. Indian chief
p. printer
q. plantation operator

Extra Challenge: Do some research into the life of one of these women, and then write a biography about her.

Phillis Wheatley

Focus on U.S. History:
The Era of Revolution and Nation-Forming

The Rights of Women

During and after the Revolution, some American women began seeking new roles and rights. But they were also very much part of eighteenth-century society, which limited women's roles and expectations. Read these passages.

Abigail Adams, writing to her husband

If particular care is not paid to the ladies, we are determined to [instigate] a rebellion, and will not hold ourselves bound by any laws in which we have no voice or representation.

That your sex are naturally tyrannical is a truth so thoroughly established as to admit of no dispute. But such of you as wish to be happy willingly give up the harsh title of master for the more tender and endearing one of friend.…Men of sense in all ages abhor those customs which treat us only as the vassals of our sex. Regard us then as beings, placed by providence under your protection, and in imitation of the Supreme Being make use of that power only for our happiness.

…with regard to the education of my own children I feel myself soon out of my depth, destitute in every part of education.…If we mean to have heroes, statesmen, and philosophers, we should have learned women.

Mercy Otis Warren

The task is easy at the same time, to be pursuing some mental improvement and yet neglect none of the duties of domestic life provided there is a methodical and uniform plan of conduct, united with an industrious mind. But how miserable must that woman be who, at the same time that she has both genius and taste for literary inquiry, can not cheerfully leave the pursuit to attend to the daily cares of the prudent housewife. Though not less to be pitied is she who is wholly immersed therein and has no higher ideas than those which confine her to the narrow circle of domestic attention. Yet a still more contemptible part of the sex are those whose lives are one uninterrupted scene of dissipation and folly.

Mercy Otis Warren

Thomas Jefferson, describing the education he wants for his daughter Patsy

[This education will be] considerably different from what I think would be most proper for her sex in any other country than America. I am obliged in it to extend my views beyond herself and consider her as possibly at the head of a little family of her own. The chance that in marriage she will draw a blockhead I calculate at about fourteen to one, and of course that the education of her family will probably rest on her own ideas and direction without assistance. With the best poets and prosewriters I shall therefore combine a certain extent of reading in the graver sciences [for her education].

(continued)

The Rights of Women *(continued)*

Directions: Identify what you have read in the passages that would urge Revolutionary-era women forward and what would hold them back.

1. Liberating new ideas expressed:

Abigail Adams

2. Limiting traditional ideas expressed:

> Lots of Revolutionary-era women didn't have much time on their hands to worry about rights, equality, education, and such things. Here's a single day in the life of young Abigail Foote, of Connecticut, in her own words, from her diary for 1776.
>
> Fix'd gown for Prude just to clear my teeth,—Mend Mother's riding-hood,—Ague in my face,—Ellen was spark'd last night,—Mother spun short thread,—Fix'd two gowns for Welch's girls,—Carded tow,—Spun linen,—Worked on cheese basket,—Hatchel'd flax with Hannah and we did 51 lb a piece,—Pleated and ironed,—Read a sermon of Dodridge's,—Spooled a piece—milked the cows—spun linen and did 50 knots—made a broom of Guinea wheat straw,—Spun thread to whiten,—Went to Mr. Otis's and made them a swinging visit,—Israel said I might ride his jade,—Set a red Dye,—Prude stayed at home and learned Eve's Dream by heart,—Had two scholars from Mrs. Taylor's—I ordered two pounds of whole wool and felt Nationly,—spun harness twine,—scoured the pewter.

Focus on U.S. History:
The Era of Revolution and Nation-Forming

Close-up: Daughters of Liberty

Many Revolutionary-era women were avid Patriots and did all they could to support the cause of independence. Here are two pictures of these women—one general, written by a Loyalist minister about all Patriot women; and one specific, about the foremost daughter of liberty.

A Maryland minister to Lord Dartmouth, Britain's Secretary of State for American Affairs

The women, both old and young, being greatly irritated at the inflexibility of administration, are not only willing their sons and brothers should turn out in the field, but also declare that they will give them up and themselves likewise as a sacrifice before they will bow to Pharaoh's taskmasters; this makes the raising of troops on the continent very easy. Let a person go into any province, city, town or county, and ask the females, "Are you willing your sons or brothers should go for soldiers and defend their liberties?" they would severally answer, "Yes, with all my soul, and if they won't go I won't own them as my sons, or brothers; for I'll help myself if there be any need of mine: if I can't stand in the ranks, I can help forward with powder, balls, and provisions."…This, my lord is the language of the American women: your lordship knows it is generally the reverse with the English, the mothers' and sisters' lives are bound up in the boys.

Mercy Otis Warren (1728–1814)

Warren used her writing skills to stir up Revolutionary feelings. This was natural, for her whole family was involved in promoting the Patriot cause, including her husband, her brother, and her father. (You've read some words of her brother James's already, in Unit 1.) Patriots often held meetings in her home. Warren's particular contribution to the revolution was satire. She wrote several plays in the 1770's (widely read but not performed in post-Puritan Massachusetts) mocking local Loyalists and British colonial government. Among these were *The Adulateur, The Defeat, The Group, The Blockheads,* and *The Motley Assembly.*

Mercy Otis Warren

Warren was tutored at home along with her brother. When he went on to higher education, she studied his college subjects at home. After the Revolution, Warren argued against the proposed Constitution as granting too much power to the federal government. She also became a noted historian, publishing the impressive three-volume *History of the Rise, Progress and Termination of the American Revolution* in 1805.

An American National Spirit

Directions: From the moment Europeans set foot on the North American continent, a new and independent culture began to grow. After Americans won the Revolutionary War, a national American culture grew.

- Find and list below examples of this new national culture.
- Then create a classroom display using those examples.

Education—examples:

Religion—examples:

Painting—examples:

Literature—examples:

Architecture—examples:

Drama—examples:

Science—examples:

Focus on U.S. History:
The Era of Revolution and Nation-Forming

Effects of the Revolution

Directions: The American Revolution had many effects on different social groups. Imagine you are each of the people named below. Tell what your revolutionary goals were—what did you hope the Revolution would accomplish, for yourself and others? Then tell what effect the Revolution had on you—socially, economically, politically.

1. You are a **white Loyalist**.

    goals: _____

    _____

    effects: _____

    _____

2. You are a **working-class lad** from New York.

    goals: _____

    _____

    effects: _____

    _____

3. You are a **Mohawk Indian** who fought with the British on the northwestern frontier.

    goals:_____

    _____

    _____

    effects: _____

    _____

    _____

Mohawk chief Joseph Brant

4. You are a **Cherokee Indian** who fought with the Americans in Tennessee.

    goals: _____

    _____

    effects: _____

    _____

(continued)

54

Focus on U.S. History:
The Era of Revolution and Nation-Forming

Effects of the Revolution *(continued)*

5. You are a **fifteen-year-old girl** who made clothing for the Continental soldiers.

   goals: _____

   _____

   effects: _____

   _____

6. You are an **African-American slave** who joined the British forces.

   goals: _____

   _____

   effects: _____

   _____

7. You are a **free African American** who enlisted in the Patriot army.

   goals: _____

   _____

   effects: _____

   _____

8. You are a **well-to-do merchant** of Boston.

   goals: _____

   _____

   effects: _____

   _____

9. You are a **small farmer** in western Pennsylvania.

   goals: _____

   _____

   effects: _____

   _____

10. You are a **married woman** who ran your husband's business while he was away at war.

    goals: _____

    _____

    effects: _____

    _____

(continued)

Creating New Governments

The objectives of this unit are to help students better understand the creation and practices of new governments in the former colonies, including the Articles of Confederation, new state constitutions, the western territory ordinances, and finally the United States Constitution and the new government it set up. Under the Articles, states kept most of their powers. They also drew up new constitutions, establishing thirteen new republican governments. The Northwest Ordinance of 1787 protected citizens' rights and provided for eventual statehood within the territory. The weakness of the national government under the Articles caused many problems, especially economic ones. People called for reform. The result was an all-new government set up by the U.S. Constitution, created by a remarkable group of delegates during the summer of 1787. This unit's activities are designed to draw students into a greater understanding of these aspects of postrevolutionary government making.

Student Activities

Mapping the New Nation uses mapping to help students visualize the changes to the political map of North America in the postrevolutionary years, up to 1802, and the problem of the British forts on the northwestern frontier.

The Articles of Confederation presents portions of Article IX of this document. Students first list powers of the national government that are listed in Article IX then deduce some rights that the states kept. The Extra Challenge asks students to identify the problems that this division of power caused for the new nation.

The Northwest Ordinance has students identify provisions of this important ordinance in particular areas. Students can answer in their own words, or you can have them answer with quotes from the Ordinance itself. The Challenge Questions show students the similarity between the Ordinance and the Bill of Rights and the inadequacy of the "utmost good faith" clause for dealings with Native Americans. The Extra Challenge has students explain the somewhat complicated procedure the Ordinance sets up for areas in the Northwest Territory.

State Constitutions is a small-group activity in which students identify features of a particular state's constitution. Groups compare findings with those of other groups investigating other state constitutions.

Postwar Economic Woes uses graphs to present economic problems that beset the new nation. Students examine the effects of each problem and explain why it helped build support for a much stronger central government.

The Delegates offers character sketches of various constitutional convention delegates written by William Pierce, an observant fellow delegate from Georgia. Students use the descriptions and further reading in role-playing a convention session.

The Slavery Debate describes some of the slave-representation debate at the convention, based on notes taken by James Madison. From the readings students create a chart of pro, con, and middle-ground positions on including slaves in population counts for representation, allowing slavery and the slave trade to continue, and taxing slaves as imports. Students learn that debate on these topics was extensive. They finish by identifying the final compromise clauses on the issues in the U.S. Constitution.

Separation of Powers uses a two-pronged approach to familiarize students with the U.S. Constitution's provisions for separation of power. Part 1 quotes the Constitution on particular powers and asks students to identify which branch of government has which power. Part 2 lists five constitutional powers and asks students to locate the words from the Constitution that grant these powers and also to identify the branch of government that has each power.

Checks and Balances is a graphic presentation of checks and balances. Students are asked to identify the corresponding check that another branch of government has on a given constitutional power. The Challenge Question asks students to explain the concept of judicial review.

In **The Fine Art of Compromise** students work in opposing groups to negotiate compromises on questions that constitutional convention delegates grappled with. After reaching their own compromise, they check to see how the Constitution's framers resolved the same issue.

Federalists and Anti-Federalists quotes the arguments of Richard Henry Lee and Alexander Hamilton on ratifying the Constitution. Using these readings and other sources, students summarize the Federalist and anti-Federalist positions. They also explain what types of people tended to favor each side and then do some research on Lee and Hamilton to find out why their backgrounds don't seem to match their positions on this issue.

Positions and Population presents U.S. population figures from the 1790 census. From these figures students predict states' positions on various constitutional issues. For an extra challenge students can use population figures to create a bar graph of the U.S. population in 1790.

Creating New Governments

The National Government: The Articles of Confederation

After they won the war, the former colonies had to create a new national government. None of the states wanted to give a lot of power to the central government, so they drew up the Articles of Confederation. It was the first constitution of the united states (which weren't called the United States yet).

Under the Articles, the states kept most of the powers. They could have their own military forces. They could make rules for trade with other states. They could issue their own money. What could the central government do? Here are a few things:

- Declare war
- Fix weights and measures
- Build and equip a navy
- Regulate Indian affairs

The State Governments

At the same time, the states drew up their own constitutions. They were mostly similar to the states' colonial charters. They usually protected people's civil rights. They called for elected legislatures, plus an executive and a court system. They limited the powers of state government. People were allowed to and expected to participate in their state governments. This was a remarkable process. For the first time ever, groups of people were peacefully drawing up their own new republican governments.

Western Lands

Maryland wouldn't sign the Articles of Confederation until all the states gave up their claims to lands west of the Appalachians. So the national government got control of this huge area. How were these new lands going to be governed? They couldn't be colonies—Americans had just fought a war about that. They couldn't be states yet—they didn't have enough people. After some hot debate, Congress passed two far-reaching and far-seeing laws about this.

Land Ordinance of 1785
- Land is surveyed into townships
- Land is sold by central government to developers
- Sections are set aside for schools in each township

Northwest Ordinance of 1787
- Sets out plan for progressive move to statehood
- Prohibits slavery
- Protects citizens' civil rights

Confederation Problems

The American economy suffered in the years right after the Revolutionary War. British manufactured goods flooded the new nation. But Britain put a lot of limits on American goods being sent to its territories. The new weak central government of America couldn't put tariffs on incoming British goods to force a change in British trade policy.

(continued)

Focus on U.S. History:
The Era of Revolution and Nation-Forming

Also, the states and the national government owed a lot of money that they'd borrowed during the war. Veterans weren't paid. People who had loaned money to the government weren't paid. The economy slid into a depression. States imposed heavy taxes. Common people were short on cash, out of work, and in debt. A group of Massachusetts farmers broke out into armed rebellion.

Things in the young nation seemed to be getting out of hand. So the states sent delegates to another convention in Philadelphia. They were supposed to fix the Articles of Confederation. Instead, they created a whole new constitution.

The United States Constitution

People all over the world are lucky that the delegates who met in Philadelphia in 1787 were so talented, thoughtful, educated, reasonable, and wise. (You'll meet some of these remarkable men in one of this unit's activities.) They thought. They debated. They compromised. And they wrote a great document that has been a pattern for governments ever since.

The delegates agreed easily on some things. Power in the new government must be balanced. No single state or section of the country must be the strongest, and no branch of the government must be the strongest. People's rights must be protected. The central government must have the right to raise taxes and to control foreign and interstate commerce.

The Representation Compromise

But how should the states be represented in the national legislature? James Madison and Edmund Randolph put forth the Virginia Plan. William Paterson offered the New Jersey Plan. Can you see why the large states favored the Virginia Plan and the small states favored the New Jersey Plan?

Virginia Plan

Representation in national legislature based on state population

New Jersey Plan

Equal representation in national legislature for each state

This became a big sticking point to the Convention. Then Roger Sherman offered the Connecticut Compromise: a House of Representatives with the number of members based on state population and a Senate in which each state has two members. The states agreed to it.

The Slave Compromise

Delegates also hotly debated the question of counting slaves. Southern states wanted slaves counted as part of the state's population when deciding how many representatives the state would have. But they didn't want slaves counted in deciding a state's share of federal taxes. Northern states wanted just the opposite.

So, the delegates worked out a rather strange compromise. Three fifths of a state's slave population would be counted for both purposes.

Other Compromises and Limits on Power

The delegates also compromised on other things, like export taxes and navigation acts. They put off the slave trade question. It was just too difficult to deal with right then.

(continued)

Focus on U.S. History:
The Era of Revolution and Nation-Forming

The proposed Constitution provided for a strong president and a national court. But Americans had just fought a war to free themselves from heavy-handed government. So, the delegates set up a clever system in the Constitution. Powers exercised by one part of the government are **checked** by other, **balancing** powers held by other parts of government. The three branches of the government—executive, legislative, and judicial—have **separate powers**.

The Fight for the Constitution

The convention sent the proposed Constitution to the states for approval in the fall of 1787. A lively debate sprang up all across the nation. People who supported the Constitution were called **Federalists**. Leading Federalists included Alexander Hamilton and James Madison. Federalists thought the nation needed a strong central government. They tended to be well-to-do, prominent citizens involved in commerce.

People who objected to the proposed Constitution were called **anti-Federalists**. Their leaders included Richard Henry Lee and Patrick Henry. They greatly feared the powers of the central government. They felt that rich and powerful interests would swallow up the common people. Individual rights would be undermined, they said. Anti-Federalists tended to be small farmers, artisans—less wealthy common people.

After all this debate, the states began to ratify the Constitution, one by one. Some acted quickly. Delaware ratified on December 7, 1787. Some dragged their heels. North Carolina signed on only in November 1789. When New Hampshire became the ninth state to ratify, on June 21, 1788, the Constitution was legally accepted. The United States of America now existed.

Carpenter's Hall, place of meeting of the First Continental Congress

Mapping the New Nation

Part 1 Directions: The new nation began to add states quickly. Adjust your map of eastern North America (page *x*) to show the following.

> - the three new states that formed in the 1790's—show boundaries; label with names and dates of statehood
> - the Northwest Territory
> - the Indiana Territory
> - the Mississippi Territory
> - land ceded to the U.S. by Georgia, 1802

State seal of Georgia

The map should still show the thirteen original states, Spanish territories, and British Canada. (You put these on the map in the Unit 2 activity *Mapping the Peace*.)

Part 2 Directions: British forts on U.S. territory remained a thorn in the new nation's side. Locate and label them on your map.

> - Dutchman's Point
> - Pointe-au-Fer
> - Oswegatchie
> - Fort Ontario
>
> - Fort Niagara
> - Detroit
> - Fort Michilimackinac

Questions:

1. Can you see why the United States objected to these forts? Explain. _____

_____

2. What treaty finally got the British to abandon the forts? _____

_____

Focus on U.S. History:
The Era of Revolution and Nation-Forming

The Articles of Confederation

Here are some of the provisions of the Articles of Confederation, which set up the first national government for the united states of America. Read the selections.

Article IX. The united states in congress assembled, shall have the sole and exclusive right and power of determining on peace and war—of sending and receiving ambassadors—entering into treaties and alliances.

The united states in congress assembled shall also be the last resort on appeal in all disputes and differences now subsisting or that hereafter may arise between two or more states concerning boundary, jurisdiction or any other cause whatever.

The united states in congress assembled shall also have the sole and exclusive right and power of . . . fixing the standard of weights and measures throughout the united states—regulating the trade and managing all affairs with the Indians . . .—establishing and regulating post-offices from one state to another, throughout all the united states, and exacting such postage on the papers passing thro' the same as may be requisite to defray the expenses of the said office—appointing all officers of the land forces in the service of the united states, excepting regimental officers—appointing all the officers of the naval forces . . . —making rules for the government and regulation of the said land and naval forces, and directing their operation.

The united states in congress assembled shall have authority to . . . build and equip a navy—to agree upon the number of land forces and to make requisitions from each state for its quota . . .

Directions: List here the powers that the national government had under the Articles of Confederation:

_____   _____
_____   _____
_____   _____

_____   _____

What powers did the states keep under the Articles of Confederation? List some here:

_____   _____
_____   _____
_____   _____
_____   _____

Extra Challenge: Why did dividing power this way cause problems for the new nation?

The Northwest Ordinance

Directions: The Northwest Ordinance of 1787 set up rules for how the western territories would be governed. They were important rules because the territories would later become states. Tell what the ordinance's provisions were in the following areas. Use your own words or quote relevant parts of the ordinance itself.

1. Practice of religion: _____

   _____

2. Justice system: _____

   _____

   _____

3. Status of slavery: _____

   _____

4. Education: _____

   _____

5. Relations with Native Americans: _____

   _____

Challenge Questions:

6. What other "document" in American history expresses the same principles as Articles 1 and 2 of the Northwest Ordinance?_____

   _____

7. How well did the "utmost good faith" clause work in practice? _____

   _____

Extra Challenge: Explain how a territory became a state as set out in the Northwest Ordinance. Why was the process set up this way?

State seal of Massachusetts

Focus on U.S. History:
The Era of Revolution and Nation-Forming

State Constitutions

State seal of North Carolina

Directions: After the Revolution, individual states drew up their own constitutions. They formed republican governments. As a member of a small group, you'll take part in a class project to investigate these state constitutions.

- Choose (or be assigned) a state to investigate.
- Study its post-Revolution constitution.
- Fill in the chart on this page.
- Compare your chart with other groups' charts.

 What <u>similarities</u> are there among the states?

 What <u>differences</u> are there?

 <u>What might account for</u> the similarities and differences?

Status of Slavery	Protection of Individual Rights
Practice of Religion	**Representation, Right to Vote**
Separation of Powers	**Type of Legislature**
Goals and Principles of Government	**Other Interesting or Notable Features**

Focus on U.S. History:
The Era of Revolution and Nation-Forming

Postwar Economic Woes

The new nation ran into a host of economic problems in the postwar years. These problems helped build pressures to change the Articles of Confederation, creating a stronger central government.

Directions: Tell what effect each economic problem noted below had on Americans and why the problem helped build support for a stronger central government.

BRITISH STOP ORDERING AMERICAN-BUILT SHIPS	STATES TAX ONE ANOTHER'S GOODS	PLANTATION LABOR SHORTAGE
Effect: _____ _____ _____ _____ _____	Effect: _____ _____ _____ _____ _____	Effect: _____ _____ _____ _____ _____
VERY HIGH STATE TAXES	STATES PRINT PAPER MONEY	BRITISH DUTY ON RICE, BAN ON IMPORTS OF INDIGO, NAVAL STORES
Effect: _____ _____ _____ _____ _____	Effect: _____ _____ _____ _____ _____	Effect: _____ _____ _____ _____ _____
CONGRESS CAN'T PAY NATIONAL DEBT OR WAGES OWED TO WAR VETERANS	BRITISH MANUFACTURED GOODS FLOOD INTO UNITED STATES	WEST INDIES TRADE CLOSED TO U.S. SHIPS
Effect: _____ _____ _____ _____ _____	Effect: _____ _____ _____ _____ _____	Effect: _____ _____ _____ _____ _____
CROP FAILURES, CASH SHORTAGES		
Effect: _____ _____ _____ _____ _____		

*Focus on U.S. History:
The Era of Revolution and Nation-Forming*

The Delegates

State seal of
Pennsylvania

Directions Part 1: William Pierce was a delegate to the constitutional convention from Georgia. He wrote descriptions of his fellow delegates. Here are some. Read them—you'll then use them for some role-playing.

George Mason, of Virginia: A gentleman of remarkable strong powers, and possesses a clear understanding. He is able and convincing in debate, steady and firm in his principles, and undoubtedly one of the best politicians in America.

Roger Sherman, of Connecticut: Exhibits the oddest shaped character I ever remember to have met with. He is awkward, unmeaning, and unaccountably strange in his manner. But in his train of thinking there is something regular, deep, and comprehensive. No man has a better heart or a clearer head. If he cannot embellish he can furnish thoughts that are wise and useful. He is an able politician.

Oliver Ellsworth, of Connecticut: He is a gentleman of a clear, deep, and copious understanding; eloquent in debate. He is very happy in a reply, and choice in selecting such parts of his adversary's arguments as [are] the strongest, in order to take off the force of them, so as to admit the power of his own.

Luther Martin, of Maryland: This gentleman possesses a good deal of information, but he has a very bad delivery, and so extremely prolix, that he never speaks without tiring the patience of all who hear him.

James Wilson, of Pennsylvania: He has joined to a fine genius all that can set him off and show him to advantage. He can trace the causes and effects of every revolution. No man is more clear, copious, and comprehensive, yet he is no great orator.

James Madison, of Virginia: In the management of every great question he took the lead, and though he cannot be called an orator, he is a most agreeable, eloquent, and convincing speaker. He always comes forward the best informed man of any point in debate. He is a gentleman of great modesty, with a remarkable sweet temper. He is easy and unreserved among his acquaintance, and has a most agreeable style of conversation.

Benjamin Franklin, of Pennsylvania: Well known to be the greatest philosopher of the present age. He does not shine much in public council—he is no speaker, nor does he seem to let politics engage his attention. He is 82 years old, and possesses an activity of mind equal to a youth of 25 years of age.

Nathaniel Gorham, of Massachusetts: A man of very good sense, but not much improved in his education. He is eloquent and easy in public debate, but has nothing fashionable or elegant in his style. All he aims at is to convince.

(continued)

The Delegates *(continued)*

Gouverneur Morris, of Pennsylvania: One of those geniuses in whom every species of talents combine to render him conspicuous and flourishing in public debate. He throws around him such a glare that he charms, captivates, and leads away the sense of all who hear him. But with all these powers he is fickle and inconstant, never pursuing one train of thinking, nor ever regular.

Charles Pinckney, of South Carolina: A young gentleman of the most promising talents. He is, although only 24 years of age, in possession of a very great variety of knowledge. He speaks with great neatness and perspicuity, and treats every subject as fully, without running into prolixity, as it requires.

Edmund Randolph, of Virginia: A young gentleman in whom unite all the accomplishments of the scholar and the statesman. He has a most harmonious voice, a fine figure and striking manners.

Rufus King, of Massachusetts: A man much distinguished for his eloquence and great parliamentary talents. In his public speaking there is something peculiarly strong and rich in his expression, clear, and convincing in his arguments, rapid and irresistible at times in his eloquence but he is not always equal. His action is natural, swimming, and graceful, but there is a rudeness of manner sometimes accompanying it.

John Dickinson, of Delaware: An indifferent speaker. With an affected air of wisdom he labors to produce a trifle; his language is irregular and incorrect; his flourishes are like expiring flames, they just show themselves and go out—no traces of them are left on the mind. He is, however, a good writer.

John Rutledge, of South Carolina: His reputation in the first Congress gave him a distinguished rank—a gentleman of distinction and fortune. He is too rapid in his public speaking to be denominated an agreeable orator.

Directions Part 2: Choose one of these characters, or another one you've found a good description of. Read all you can about your character, so you can act the way he probably did at the constitutional convention. Then, with classmates, role-play one of the sessions at the convention, discussing one of the thorny problems they had to settle in creating the Constitution. Remember, it is very hot in Philadelphia, which might tend to make people grumpy.

Name _____

Date _____

The Slavery Debate

The delegates at the constitutional convention had a great debate on the question of counting slaves as part of a state's population in figuring how many seats that state would have in the House of Representatives. Delegates from northern and southern states expressed their views on slavery and the slave trade. Here are some parts of this debate, from notes taken at the constitutional convention by James Madison.

Gouverneur Morris (Pennsylvania): He never would concur in upholding domestic slavery. It was the curse of heaven on the states where it prevailed.... Upon what principle is it that the slaves shall be computed in the representation? Are they men? Then make them citizens, and let them vote. Are they property? Why, then, is no other property included? ...The admission of slaves into the representation ...comes fairly to this,—that the inhabitant of Georgia and South Carolina, who goes to the coast of Africa, and, in defiance of the most sacred laws of humanity, tears away his fellow-creatures from their dearest connections, and damns them to the most cruel bondage, shall have more votes, in a government instituted for the protection of the rights of mankind, than the citizen of Pennsylvania or New Jersey, who views, with a laudable horror, so nefarious a practice.

Luther Martin (Maryland): In the first place, as five slaves are to be counted as three freemen, in the apportionment of representatives, such a clause would leave an encouragement to this traffic. In the second place, slaves weakened one part of the Union, which the other parts were bound to protect; the privilege of importing them was therefore unreasonable. And, in the third place, it was inconsistent with the principles of the revolution, and dishonorable to the American character, to have such a feature in the Constitution.

John Rutledge (South Carolina): He was not apprehensive of insurrections, and would readily exempt the other states from the obligation to protect the southern [states] against them. Religion and humanity had nothing to do with this question. Interest alone is the governing principle with nations.... If the Convention thinks that North Carolina, South Carolina, and Georgia will ever agree to the plan, unless their right to import slaves be untouched, the expectation is vain. The people of those states will never be such fools as to give up so important an interest.

Oliver Ellsworth (Connecticut): Let every state import what it pleases. The morality or wisdom of slavery are considerations belonging to the states themselves. What enriches a part enriches the whole, and the states are the best judges of their particular interest.... Let us not intermeddle. As population increases, poor laborers will be so plenty as to render slaves useless. Slavery, in time, will not be a speck in our country.

State seal of Connecticut

(continued)

Focus on U.S. History:
The Era of Revolution and Nation-Forming

The Slavery Debate *(continued)*

Roger Sherman (Connecticut): He disapproved of the slave trade; yet, as the states were now possessed of the right to import slaves, as the public good did not require it to be taken from them, and as it was expedient to have as few objections as possible to the proposed scheme of government, he thought it best to leave the matter as we find it. He observed, that the abolition of slavery seemed to be going on in the United States, and that the good sense of the several states would probably by degrees complete it.

George Mason (Virginia): [The slave trade is an] infernal traffic. . . . Slavery discourages arts and manufactures. The poor despise labor when performed by slaves. . . . Every master of slaves is born a petty tyrant. [Slaves] bring the judgment of Heaven on a country. . . . By an inevitable chain of causes and effects, Providence punishes national sins by national calamities.

Charles Pinckney (South Carolina): He contended that the importation of slaves would be for the interest of the whole Union. The more slaves, the more produce to employ the carrying trade; the more consumption also; and the more of this, the more revenue for the common treasury. He admitted it to be reasonable that slaves should be dutied like other imports.

State seal of Virginia

Rufus King (Massachusetts): He remarked on the exemption of slaves from duty, whilst every other import was subjected to it, as an inequality that could not fail to strike the commercial sagacity of the Northern and Middle states

John Dickinson (Delaware): He considered it as inadmissible, on every principle of honor and safety, that the importation of slaves should be authorized to the states by the Constitution.

Directions: These delegates were concerned with several interrelated issues: counting slaves for purposes of representation, allowing slavery and the slave trade to continue, and taxing slaves as imports. Make a chart with those issues as headings. Under each, summarize the various positions that delegates expressed on that issue—pro, con, and middle ground. Note at the bottom of each column the final compromise that the delegates reached on the issue by quoting the compromise clause from the U.S. Constitution.

Challenge Question: What is odd about George Mason's antislavery declarations?

Name _____

Date _____

Separation of Powers

The U.S. Constitution set up a system with three main branches of government—the **executive** (headed by the president), the **legislative** (the House of Representatives and the Senate), and the **judiciary** (the federal court system). Each branch is separate from the others. Each branch has its own powers.

Part 1 Directions: Here are some quotations from the Constitution that describe particular powers. For each, tell which branch of the government has this constitutional power.

1. Shall have the sole power to try all impeachments: _____

2. Shall have power to establish post offices and post roads: _____

3. Shall take care that the laws be faithfully executed: _____

4. Power shall extend to controversies between two or more states: _____

5. Shall have power to grant reprieves and pardons for offenses against the United States:

   _____

6. Shall have power to define and punish piracies and felonies committed on the high seas:

   _____

7. Power shall extend to all cases arising under the laws of the United States:

   _____

8. Shall have power to make treaties: _____

9. Shall have power to declare war: _____

Part 2 Directions: Some constitutional powers are listed below. Get a copy of the U.S. Constitution. Then, on the lines provided, write the words from the Constitution giving that power, and tell which branch of government the power applies to.

1. Can disapprove laws passed by another branch: _____

   _____

2. Can impose and collect taxes: _____

   _____

3. Decides cases between citizens of different states: _____

   _____

4. Can raise and pay for an army and a navy: _____

   _____

5. Commands the army and the navy: _____

   _____

Name _____

Date _____

Checks and Balances

The framers of the Constitution didn't want any one branch of the government to be too strong. So they set up a system in which each branch **checks** (holds back) the power of the other two branches. One branch's powers are **balanced** by the powers of the other two branches. This is called the system of **checks and balances**.

Directions: To see how the system works, name a check on each power listed below.

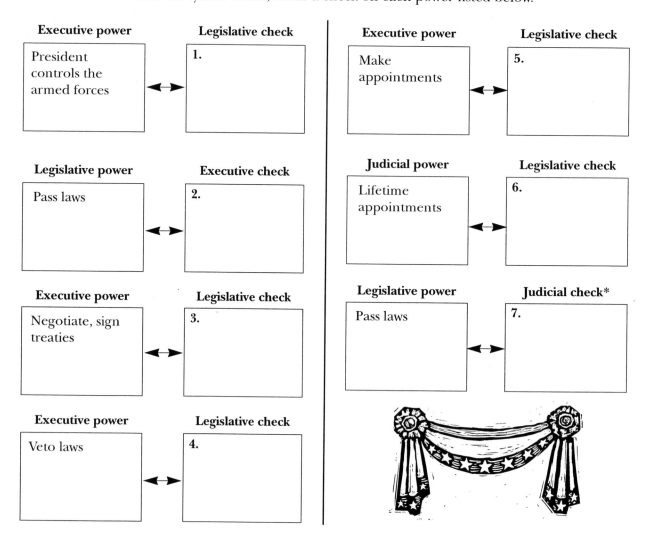

Executive power

President controls the armed forces

Legislative check

1.

Legislative power

Pass laws

Executive check

2.

Executive power

Negotiate, sign treaties

Legislative check

3.

Executive power

Veto laws

Legislative check

4.

Executive power

Make appointments

Legislative check

5.

Judicial power

Lifetime appointments

Legislative check

6.

Legislative power

Pass laws

Judicial check*

7.

Challenge Question: The judicial check marked with an asterisk (*) isn't spelled out in the Constitution. Where does this powerful check come from?

*Focus on U.S. History:
The Era of Revolution and Nation-Forming*

The Fine Art of Compromise

Directions: The framers of the U.S. Constitution knew that in order to succeed, they would have to **compromise.** No state or group of people could get all they wanted in the new national government they were creating. Below are opposite positions on constitutional issues. You will be assigned to one side or the other. Your job is to negotiate with classmates on the opposite side to reach a compromise you can all live with. After you reach your compromise, note how the Constitution's framers compromised on this issue.

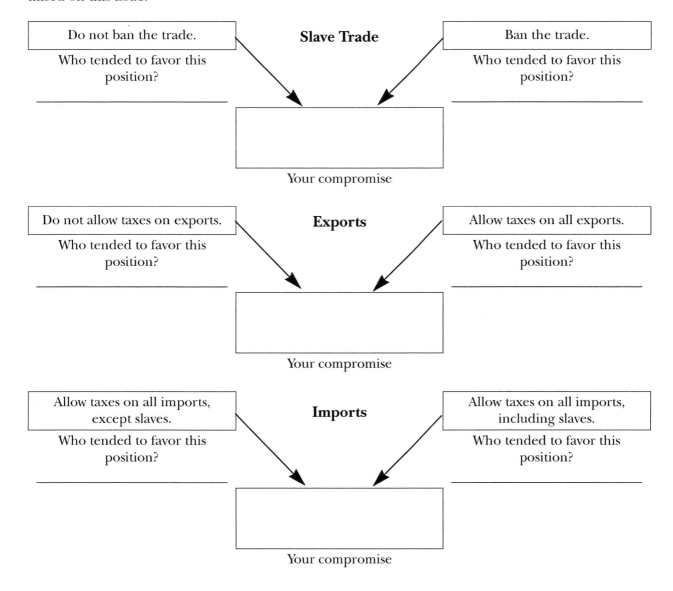

| Do not ban the trade. | **Slave Trade** | Ban the trade. |

Who tended to favor this position? _____

Who tended to favor this position? _____

Your compromise

| Do not allow taxes on exports. | **Exports** | Allow taxes on all exports. |

Who tended to favor this position? _____

Who tended to favor this position? _____

Your compromise

| Allow taxes on all imports, except slaves. | **Imports** | Allow taxes on all imports, including slaves. |

Who tended to favor this position? _____

Who tended to favor this position? _____

Your compromise

Focus on U.S. History:
The Era of Revolution and Nation-Forming

Federalists and Anti-Federalists

People who wanted the proposed Constitution accepted by the states were called **Federalists**. People who opposed the Constitution were called **anti-Federalists**. Here are some of their views.

◆●◆━━◆●◆

Richard Henry Lee, of Virginia (1787):

The plan of government now proposed is evidently calculated totally to change, in time, our condition as a people. Instead of being thirteen republics, under a federal head, it is clearly designed to make us one consolidated government. . . . [There is a] strong tendency to aristocracy now discernible in every part of the plan. [There is a] great . . . accumulation of powers, especially as to the internal police of this country in a few hands. . . . [O]ne government alone never can extend equal benefits to all parts of the United States: Different laws, customs, and opinions exist in the different states, which by a uniform system of laws would be unreasonably invaded.

State seal of Virginia

◆●◆━━◆●◆

Alexander Hamilton, of New York (1787–88):

. . . [T]he prosperity of America depend[s] on its Union. To preserve and perpetuate it was the great object of the . . . plan which the convention has advised [the people] to adopt. . . . The powers delegated by the proposed Constitution to the federal government are few and defined. Those which are to remain in the state governments are numerous and indefinite. . . . The powers reserved to the several states will extend to all the objects which, in the ordinary course of affairs, concern the lives, liberties, and properties of the people, and the internal order, improvement, and prosperity of the state.

◆●◆━━◆●◆

Directions:

1. Use what you have read above, and in other sources, to summarize the positions of the Federalists and the anti-Federalists. What types of people tended to favor each side?

2. Read about the lives of Richard Henry Lee and Alexander Hamilton. What about the background of each man makes his position on adopting the new Constitution rather odd?

Focus on U.S. History:
The Era of Revolution and Nation-Forming

Positions and Population

Directions: Here are population figures for the thirteen original states. Use them to predict the states' positions on Constitutional questions. (The population figures are from the 1790 census, taken just three years after the Constitution was written.)

State seal of Massachusetts

U.S. Population, 1790 Census*

State	Total	White	Black
Connecticut	239,000	233,000	6,000
Delaware	59,000	46,000	13,000
Georgia	83,000	53,000	30,000
Maine (part of Massachusetts)	97,000	96,000	1,000
Maryland	320,000	209,000	111,000
Massachusetts	378,000	373,000	5,000
New Hampshire	143,000	142,000	1,000
New Jersey	184,000	170,000	14,000
New York	340,000	314,000	26,000
North Carolina	394,000	288,000	106,000
Pennsylvania	434,000	424,000	10,000
Rhode Island	69,000	65,000	4,000
South Carolina	249,000	140,000	109,000
Virginia	748,000	442,000	306,000

* Figures, as reported in the Historical Statistics of the United States, Vol. 1 (Washington, DC: U.S. Department of Commerce, Bureau of the Census, 1975), do not always add up.

(continued)

Positions and Population *(continued)*

State seal of
New Jersey

Directions: Have your chart of 1790 population figures on hand. Use those figures to answer these questions about states' positions on issues the framers of the U.S. Constitution had to wrestle with. Refer back to page 60 for questions 1 and 2.

1. Which states' delegates do you think would have supported the Virginia Plan for the Constitution? Why?

    States: _____

    Reasons: _____

    _____

2. Which states' delegates do you think would have supported the New Jersey Plan for the Constitution? Why?

    States: _____

    Reasons: _____

    _____

3. Which states' delegates might be most willing to compromise between those two plans? Why?

    States: _____

    Reasons: _____

    _____

4. Which states' delegates might have been most likely to want slaves counted in determining how many representatives those states would have? Why?

    States: _____

    Reasons: _____

    _____

5. Which states' delegates might have been most likely to want slaves counted in figuring each state's share of federal taxes? Why?

    States: _____

    Reasons: _____

    _____

Extra Challenge: Use these figures to create a bar graph of U.S. population by state in 1790, showing black, white, and total population.

Fine-tuning the System

The objectives of this unit are to give students a better understanding of the guarantees of the Bill of Rights, of how the American political party system was born, and of how the new Supreme Court grew in power and significance. Many people were concerned about protecting civil liberties under the proposed Constitution, and the outcome was the Bill of Rights, the first ten amendments to the Constitution. The Constitution didn't envision political parties, but sharp differences between Alexander Hamilton and Thomas Jefferson spurred distinct parties to form around each man. Factional differences led Congress to pass the Alien and Sedition Acts of 1798, which threatened First Amendment rights. Within a few years, however, the Supreme Court emerged as a powerful force, able to strike down unconstitutional laws and protect citizens against extreme acts of Congress. The activities in this unit promote student understanding of how the young nation fine-tuned its new institutions and systems.

Student Activities

The Bill of Rights presents original text of several constitutional amendments and asks students to identify which rights each amendment guarantees and then give an example of these rights being exercised in contemporary life. Next, students respond to questions by quoting from the Bill of Rights. Challenge Questions are open-ended and thought provoking, centering on First Amendment, Second Amendment, and due-process rights.

Why a Bill of Rights? again quotes Richard Henry Lee and Alexander Hamilton, this time speaking about whether the U.S. Constitution needed a bill of rights. Students use these and other sources to contrast the opposing positions on this question. For an extra challenge students can role-play a debate between Federalists and anti-Federalists on the subject.

The Sedition Act quotes Section 2 of the act and leads students into analyzing why it was passed, how it may have violated freedom of speech and of the press, and how proponents justified such violations.

Students complete the activity by deciding whether or not the act was unconstitutional.

Hamilton versus Jefferson provides a frame to examine differences between the two political leaders in a number of areas. The Extra Challenge invites students to role-play a discussion or debate between these two very opposite men.

In **Which Political Party?** students imagine themselves to be particular people of the 1790's to decide which political party they will support, Hamilton's Federalists or Jefferson's Republicans.

Close-up: A Pair of Rebellions summarizes Shays' Rebellion and the Whiskey Rebellion. Students are asked to locate the context in which Jefferson remarked, "a little rebellion now and then is a good thing," and explain why Jefferson felt this way.

The Rebellions: A Closer Look is a chart on which students identify political, economic, social, and geographic factors that caused each rebellion.

Challenge Questions ask students to find a pattern in the rebellions and see how it applies to the four rebellions they studied in Unit 3 of the second book in this series (Worksheets 2 and 3, Close-up: Bacon's Rebellion and Others and Colonial Rebellions, pages 37 and 38).

Supreme Court Power familiarizes students with three key decisions that established the Supreme Court's power and expanded the national government's power. The Challenge Question invites students to think about whether the Supreme Court's power is a positive or negative force in the American political system.

Treaty Making shows students that the new nation was quickly involved in making treaties, both with Native Americans and with foreign powers, and was showing signs of expansionism already in the 1790's. Students examine specific provisions of four treaties and review their knowledge of the treaty-making provisions of the U.S. Constitution.

Fine-tuning the System

The Bill of Rights

During the debate about accepting the Constitution, many people expressed concern about civil liberties. Would the national government be able to deny citizens freedom of religion or of the press? What about trial by jury? Would the states really keep most of their rights?

Some Federalists (supporters of the Constitution) claimed that the document already protected the rights of people and states. Others weren't so sure. So, backers of the Constitution promised to add amendments guaranteeing civil liberties and states' powers.

Congressman James Madison wrote the amendments in 1789. Ten were soon ratified. Together they are called the Bill of Rights. They guarantee a broad spectrum of individual and states' rights. Here are some of the most important:

- Freedom of religion
- Freedom of the press
- Freedom of speech
- Trial by jury
- Right to bear arms
- No unreasonable searches or seizures

The broadest guarantee for individuals is in the Fifth Amendment, which states that no person can be "deprived of life, liberty, or property, without due process of law." Also, the Tenth Amendment states that all powers not specifically given to the central government or specifically denied to the states in the Constitution remain with the states or the people.

The Bill of Rights is a cornerstone of American freedom. Its words are often used to decide court cases today.

The Rise of Political Parties

George Washington became the first president of the United States. He worked hard to set a good example for future presidents. He brought dignity and strength to the office. He was very careful not to exercise more power than he thought the Constitution gave the president.

Washington also tried hard to be nonpartisan, but it wasn't easy. His two top advisers were Alexander Hamilton and Thomas Jefferson. They disagreed about all sorts of policy questions.

Thomas Jefferson

Alexander Hamilton

Hamilton	Jefferson
• Strong central government	• Strong state governments
• Economy: commerce and manufacturing	• Economy: farming
• Federal powers: broad	• Federal powers: narrow

(continued)

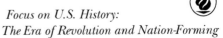

The Constitution does not mention political parties. But they started forming quickly around these two leaders. Hamilton's was the **Federalist** party. Jefferson's was the **Republican** party. (At first, it was called the Democratic Republican party.)

Federalists tended to be well-off businessmen, large landowners, and professional people who admired British society and government. Republicans tended to be farmers and "common people." They admired the new revolution in France.

John Adams

John Adams, a Federalist, was elected the second U.S. president in 1796. In an odd twist of the electoral college, Republican Thomas Jefferson was elected vice president.

The Alien and Sedition Acts

Meanwhile, relations with France were not going well. French vessels attacked American ships. The French foreign minister, Talleyrand, demanded a bribe to stop the attacks. Americans were outraged.

Federalists saw a chance to strike at the Republicans. They passed the Alien and Sedition Acts in 1798. The three alien acts were aimed at anti-Federalist nationals living in the United States. The Sedition Act was an attempt to silence Republican newspapers and their attacks on Federalists. Editors and publishers were fined and jailed for publishing "false, scandalous and malicious" descriptions of government actions and officials.

The Sedition Act was a serious challenge to the First Amendment rights of freedom of the press and freedom of speech. The act expired in 1800.

The Supreme Court

Of the three branches of government, the Constitution says least about the judicial system. John Marshall became Chief Justice of the Supreme Court in 1801. Under him, the Court grew into an equal, and equally powerful, branch of government, which strengthened national government as a whole.

John Marshall

The first key decision came in 1803, in *Marbury* v. *Madison*. Marshall used this case to establish the principle of **judicial review**. If Congress passed a law that violated the Constitution, Marshall wrote, that law was struck down. It wasn't a valid law.

The Sedition Act stands as an example of why the Supreme Court's principle of judicial review was so important and needed to protect Constitutional rights. Still, the Court never ruled on the Sedition Act. It's interesting to think about what the decision would have been.

The Bill of Rights

Part 1 Directions: The Bill of Rights is actually the first ten amendments to the U.S. Constitution. Explain in your own words what important right(s) each amendment below guarantees to the American people. Then give an example of this right being exercised today, preferably in your own school, home, or community.

Amendment 1: Congress shall make no law respecting an establishment of religion, or prohibiting the free exercise thereof; or abridging the freedom of speech, or of the press, or the right of the people peaceably to assemble, and to petition the government for a redress of grievances.

Right #1:_____

Example: _____

Right #2: _____

Example: _____

Right #3: _____

Example: _____

Right #4: _____

Example: _____

Amendment 2: A well-regulated Militia, being necessary to the security of a free State, the right of the people to keep and bear Arms, shall not be infringed.

Right: _____

Example: _____

Amendment 4: The right of the people to be secure in their persons, houses, papers, and effects, against unreasonable searches and seizures, shall not be violated, and no Warrants shall issue, but upon probable cause, supported by Oath or affirmation, and particularly describing the place to be searched, and the persons or things to be seized.

Right: _____

Example: _____

(continued)

The Bill of Rights *(continued)*

Amendment 8: Excessive bail shall not be required, nor excessive fines imposed, nor cruel and unusual punishments inflicted.

Right: _____

_____

Example: _____

_____

Part 2 Directions: Now find a copy of the Bill of Rights yourself. Read it, and then answer these questions.

1. Can you be tried twice for the same offense? _____ Quote the part of the Bill of

   Rights that covers this: _____

   _____

2. What abuses of the justice system is the Sixth Amendment designed to prevent?

   _____

   _____

3. What recent abuses in the colonies is the Third Amendment designed to prevent?

   _____

   _____

4. Can you be forced to testify against yourself in a court case? _____

   Quote the part of the Bill of Rights that covers this: _____

   _____

(continued)

The Bill of Rights *(continued)*

5. Which amendment contains the due process clause? _____

    Quote that clause: _____

    _____

    _____

Challenge Questions:

6. Are there any limits on the right of free speech?

7. Why is a ban on certain types of guns not a violation of the Second Amendment?

8. Why is the due process clause so important?

Focus on U.S. History:
The Era of Revolution and Nation-Forming

Why a Bill of Rights?

Directions: Federalists (who supported the new Constitution) and anti-Federalists (who were against the Constitution) had different opinions. One big thing they differed on was the need to protect individual rights in the Constitution. Here are arguments on both sides of the issue.

Richard Henry Lee, Virginia patriot and anti-Federalist (1787)
But what is the power given to this ill-constructed body [the House of Representatives]? To judge of what may be for the *general welfare,* and such judgment, when made with that of Congress, is to be *the supreme law of the land.* This seems to be a power co-extensive with every possible object of human legislation. Yet there is no restraint, in form of a bill of rights, to secure ... that residuum of human rights which is not meant to be given up to society, and which, indeed, is not necessary to be given for any good social purpose. The rights of conscience, the freedom of the press, and the trial by jury, are at mercy.

Alexander Hamilton, New York patriot and Federalist (1787–88)
... [T]hough the constitution of New York has no bill of rights prefixed to it, yet it contains in the body of it various provisions in favor of particular privileges and rights which, in substance, amount to the same thing. ... [T]he Constitution proposed by the convention contains, as well as the constitution of this state, a number of such provisions. ...

I go further and affirm that bills of rights ... are not only unnecessary in the proposed Constitution but would even be dangerous ... For why declare that things shall not be done which there is no power to do? Why, for instance, should it be said that the liberty of the press shall not be restrained when no power is given by which restrictions may be imposed?

Alexander Hamilton

Directions: Use the passages above and other reading you have done to answer these questions.

1. Why did the Constitution need a bill of rights, according to the anti-Federalists?

2. Why did the Constitution *not* need a bill of rights, according to the Federalists?

3. What do you think? Is it a good thing that the Bill of Rights was added to the Constitution?

Extra Challenge: Role-play a debate between Federalists and anti-Federalists on this subject.

84

*Focus on U.S. History:
The Era of Revolution and Nation-Forming*

The Sedition Act

Directions: The Alien and Sedition Acts, passed in 1798, were aimed against anti-Federalist writers. Here is the most important part of Section 2 of the Sedition Act. It's one very, very, very long sentence. Break it down into parts to make it more understandable.

Section 2. That if any person shall write, print, utter, or publish, or shall cause or procure to be written, printed, uttered, or published, or shall knowingly and willingly assist or aid in writing, printing, uttering, or publishing any false, scandalous and malicious writing or writings against the government of the United States, or either house of the Congress of the United States, or the President of the United States, with intent to defame the said government, or either house of the said Congress, or the said President, or to bring them, or either of them, into contempt or disrepute; or to excite against them, or either or any of them, the hatred of the good people of the United States, or to excite any unlawful combinations therein, for opposing or resisting any law of the United States, or any act of the President of the United States, done in pursuance of any such constitution of the United States, or to resist, oppose, or defeat any such law or act ... then such person being thereof convicted before any court of the United States having jurisdiction thereof shall be punished by a fine not exceeding two thousand dollars, and by imprisonment not exceeding two years.

Questions:

1. Wow! You've read the First Amendment to the Constitution, about freedom of the press and of speech. In what ways, if any, do you think this act violates those freedoms?

2. Why was this act passed?

3. How did the people who had this act passed justify it—why did they think (or say) it wasn't a violation of the Bill of Rights?

4. What do you think? Was this act constitutional? (The courts never did rule on it.)

Hamilton Versus Jefferson

Directions: Alexander Hamilton and Thomas Jefferson had very different opinions about a lot of things. Hamilton was a leading **Federalist**. Jefferson was a leading **anti-Federalist**. Describe their different views on issues below.

Hamilton	views on	Jefferson
	Strict versus loose interpretation of Constitution	
	National bank	
	Paying the national debt from the war	
	The American economy	
	British society and government	
	France's revolution	
	The central government	

Extra Challenge: Role-play a discussion or a debate between Jefferson and Hamilton on one of these issues.

Focus on U.S. History:
The Era of Revolution and Nation-Forming

Which Political Party?

Directions: The followers of Hamilton and Jefferson grouped together to form the new nation's first political parties—the **Federalists** and the **Republicans** (first called the Democratic Republicans). Read about the stands those parties took. Then imagine you are each of the people described below. Which party might you join? Why?

1. You are an aristocratic **South Carolina plantation owner.**

2. You are a well-to-do **New York merchant.**

3. You are **building a homestead** for your family in **Kentucky.**

4. You **distill whiskey** on your farm in western **Pennsylvania.**

5. You are a **banker in Philadelphia.**

6. You are a **Connecticut veteran of the Revolutionary War**, and you haven't lost your revolutionary fervor.

7. You're a **small merchant** in debt to creditors. You've had to sell your Confederation securities for very little to a speculator.

8. You're a **prominent Virginia lawyer.**

Thomas Jefferson

Alexander Hamilton

Close-up: A Pair of Rebellions

The colonial period of American history saw several rebellions—Bacon's (1676), Leisler's (1689), the Paxton Boys' (1763), and the Carolina Regulators (1771). The new nation saw a pair of rebellions as well.

Shays' Rebellion

To pay off its Revolutionary War debt, the state of Massachusetts imposed high taxes. Average people were hit the hardest. Farmers had to pay as much as one third of their annual income to the state. Many fell into debt. Then creditors from the eastern part of the state insisted on being paid what they were owed. Lenders foreclosed mortgages and seized farmers' land and buildings. Debt-ridden farmers ended up in jail.

Daniel Shays, a western Massachusetts farmer, got fed up. He had fought in the war, at places like Bunker Hill and Saratoga. He led hundreds of fellow farmers in a rebellion in 1786 and 1787. Mobs stopped courts from holding foreclosure proceedings. Shays and his men marched on Springfield and stopped a session of the state supreme court. They stormed the federal arsenal in Springfield, but the state militia repelled and defeated them. Shays was sentenced to death, but he escaped to Vermont. He and most of his men were pardoned within a year.

Whiskey Rebellion

In 1791 the United States imposed an excise tax on whiskey, recommended by Alexander Hamilton. The tax hit western Pennsylvania farmers hard. Many of them grew grain, and they distilled a lot of that grain into whiskey. They felt unfairly targeted by the tax, and their strong feelings led to organized resistance and violence. They refused to pay the tax. In 1794, mobs tarred and feathered revenue agents and burned their homes. One person was killed. Thousands of "whiskey rebels" marched on Pittsburgh.

President Washington became alarmed. At his request, the governors of Virginia, Pennsylvania, Maryland, and New Jersey mobilized their state militias. Washington ordered a huge force of militiamen into western Pennsylvania. The rebellion immediately melted away. Most participants who were arrested were let go for lack of evidence.

The so-called Whiskey Rebellion showed that the new national government could and would enforce its laws. It put into action for the first time the president's power to call up the state militias for federal purposes.

Thomas Jefferson's reaction to the Whiskey Rebellion was: "I hold it that a little rebellion now and then is a good thing, and as necessary in the political world as storms in the physical."

Why did he say this? Find the original quote. Jefferson's second sentence gives the answer.

The Rebellions: A Closer Look

Directions: Several different factors combined to cause the rebellions you've just read about. Use what you've learned to fill in this chart.

	Shays' Rebellion	**Whiskey Rebellion**
Political Factors		
Economic Factors		
Social Factors		
Geographic Factors		

Challenge Questions:

1. Do you see a pattern to these two rebellions? Describe it.

2. Did you complete the Colonial Rebellions activity sheet in Unit 3 of the second book in this series, *The Era of Colonization and Settlement*? In that activity, you compared four colonial rebellions. Get out the chart you completed for that activity. Do you see any continuing pattern among all six of these rebellions?

Supreme Court Power

Directions: The Constitution didn't give the Supreme Court much explicit power. But a series of Court decisions made the Court an equal power in the three-branch U.S. government. (This happened after the early constitutional period, from 1803 to the 1820's.) Explain how these Court decisions increased the Supreme Court's power as well as the power of the national government.

Marbury* v. *Madison Decision: Increase in Supreme Court power:	Summary of case:
McCulloch* v. *Maryland Decision: Increase in Supreme Court power: Increase in national government power:	Summary of case:
Gibbons* v. *Ogden Decision: Increase in Supreme Court power: Increase in national government power:	Summary of case:

Challenge Question: Why is it a good—or a bad—thing that the Supreme Court is so powerful?

Focus on U.S. History:
The Era of Revolution and Nation-Forming

Treaty Making

Directions: The new nation was soon engaged in making treaties to settle problems with foreign nations. Identify details of the following treaties.

Treaty of Greenville (1795)

Between U.S. and _____

U.S. gains:

Treaty of Fort Stanwix (1784)

Between U.S. and _____

U.S. gains:

Pinckney's Treaty (1795)

Formal name:

Between U.S. and _____

U.S. gains:

Jay's Treaty (1795)

Between U.S. and _____

U.S. gains:

Review Questions:

1. Under the Constitution, which element of government has the power to make treaties?

2. Under the Constitution, which element of government has the power to approve treaties?

Focus on U.S. History:
The Era of Revolution and Nation-Forming

United States Capitol

ANSWER KEY
ADDITIONAL ACTIVITIES
ASSESSMENTS

Unit 1: The Road to War

The Peace of Paris (page 6)

Great Britain after 1763: 13 colonies, west to Appalachian Mountains; Canada; eastern Mississippi Valley; Florida

France after 1763: Guadeloupe and Martinique

Spain after 1763: New Orleans; Cuba; North America west of Mississippi River

Challenge Question: England changed its policy of "salutary neglect" of the colonies; began attempts to tax colonies and tighten administrative control of them. Started down the road to revolution.

Steps to Revolution (page 7)

Items should be numbered, in order: 4, 8, 13, 2, 7, 16, 9, 6, 3, 10, 14, 11, 5, 1, 15, 12

Answer: George Washington

Voices of Dissent (page 8)

Major objections: Invasion of homes via writs of assistance (violation of civil rights); Parliament makes laws that are binding on the colonies and imposes taxes on the colonies, even though colonies have no voice in Parliament; British government interferes with colonists' self-government and declares that Parliament is the supreme authority; troops are quartered in a country at peace.

Voices of Consent (page 10)

Main points: Colonies must expect and accept some control by mother country, which includes some restrictions on "English liberties"; the mother country, by its nature, has control of her colonies, which must be subordinate; the colonies cannot be equally represented in Parliament because thousands of miles separate England and the colonies; Intolerable/Coercive Acts are proper response to colonists' unlawful and rebellious behavior; British government has right to tax colonies because people enjoying the protection of British power must help pay for that; British government has right to regulate trade within the Empire.

Understanding the Declaration of Independence (page 16)

Assign one or more of these phrases to each group, with a stated amount of time to complete their explanations. Then have groups share their explanations with the rest of the class. Discuss. Does everyone agree? Opinions on explanations are likely to vary on "all men are created equal" in particular.

Why Independence? (page 17)

1. The Virginia, New York, and Massachusetts legislatures were all dissolved at various times.

2. Standing armies remained in the colonies after the French and Indian War ended, even though no foreign enemy was present to defend the colonies against, other than Spain in the far South.

3. a. The Quartering Act required local legislatures to pay for housing and feeding British troops stationed in the colonies.

b. Most of the soldiers who killed colonists at the Boston Massacre were acquitted, and the others were not punished severely.

c. The Coercive Acts closed Boston Harbor; after the war began, Britain used its control of the seas to shut down colonial trade.

d. As part of administering the Townshend duties, new courts were set up that tried cases related to the duties without juries.

e. The Townshend duty courts operated in Halifax as well as in the colonies; the Coercive Acts allowed cases to be transferred outside of Massachusetts at the governor's discretion.

f. The Massachusetts Government Act, one of the Coercive Acts, did this.

g. This was part of the Coercive Acts.

4. This describes early naval actions during the war; for example, British naval forces attacked and burned Falmouth (later Portland), Maine.

5. The British Army employed Hessians—German soldiers—in the war; using mercenaries against the colonists convinced many to support independence.

6. When British Navy forces captured American ships, they declared the American seamen to be English citizens and therefore bound to serve in the British armed forces.

7. In November 1775, the royal governor of Virginia, Lord Dunmore, promised freedom to all slaves who would fight with the British Army. The British also encouraged their Indian allies to take up arms against the colonists during the war.

Slavery and the Declaration of Independence (page 19)

Challenge Question: First, Georgia and South Carolina insisted on their right to continue the slave trade. Second, northern seafarers participated heavily in the slave trade, transporting Africans to the colonies and making a lot of money out of it.

Additional Activity Suggestions

You could have students do any of the following activities.

1. Add the Proclamation of 1763 line to the post-French and Indian War map you completed as the Extra Challenge activity for The Peace of Paris.

2. Was the break with England avoidable? Individually or as a member of a small group, list a number of different decisions that could have been made, steps taken or not taken on both sides that might have prevented the colonies from breaking with the mother country.

3. Deliver Patrick Henry's "Liberty or Death" speech to the class. Your objective is to deliver the speech with as much dramatic flair as Henry did. Here's how one person who was present at Henry's oration described it:

"Henry rose with an unearthly fire burning in his eye. He commenced somewhat calmly, but the smothered excitement began more and more to play upon his features and thrill in the tones of his voice. The tendons of his neck stood out white and rigid like whipcords. His voice rose louder and louder, until the walls of the building, and all within them, seemed to shake and rock in its tremendous vibrations. Finally his pale face and glaring eyes became terrible to look upon. Men leaned forward in their seats, with their heads strained forward, their faces pale, and their eyes glaring like the speaker's. His last exclamation, 'Give me liberty or give me death!' was like the shout of the leader which turns back the rout of battle."

4. Explain the sources of the ideas expressed in the Declaration of Independence, such as Enlightenment thought, English common law and bill of rights, and natural law concepts.

5. Identify revolutions in other parts of the world that have been influenced by the Declaration of Independence.

Unit 1 Assessment

1. Write an essay in which you discuss whether it was reasonable for England to tax the colonists to help pay for the French and Indian

War and for costs of administering the colonies, and whether Americans were justified in objecting to these taxes and other English policies toward the colonies after 1763.

2. Trace the chain of events from 1763 that led up to the confrontation at Lexington and Concord. After the events at Lexington and Concord, could war have been avoided? If so, how? If not, why not?

3. The Extra Challenge role-play for the Loyalist or Patriot? activity sheet would be a useful assessment tool for overall class assessment.

Unit 2: Fighting the War

The War: Time Line and Mapping (page 25)

1. April 1775. British fire on militiamen, killing eight, at Lexington; fight with colonials at Concord; are shot down by colonials on retreat to Boston.

2. May 1775. Ethan Allen, Benedict Arnold, and the Green Mountain Boys capture Fort Ticonderoga on Lake Champlain.

3. December 1775. British forces at Quebec fight off Arnold and Montgomery.

4. May 1775. Meets in Philadelphia, names George Washington commander-in-chief of Continental Army, starts requisitioning arms and supplies.

5. June 1775. American forces drive off attacking British regulars twice and then retreat when they run out of ammunition (actual battle on Breed's Hill).

6. June 1775. Named by the Continental Congress and then leaves for Massachusetts and siege of Boston.

7. December 1776. Washington and his troops cross the Delaware River, surprise Hessians, and defeat them at Trenton, New Jersey.

8. March 1776. General Howe withdraws British troops from encircled Boston to Halifax, Nova Scotia.

9. August 1776. Howe, returned to America, soundly defeats Washington's forces in New York.

10. July 1776. The final break with England.

11. September 1776. The British drive Washington out of New York City, occupying a major American urban center.

12. September–October 1777. Colonial forces under Horatio Gates defeat British troops led by General Burgoyne; British plan to control Hudson River and split the Colonies fails.

13. September 1777. General Howe moves into the city after defeating Washington at Brandywine, spends winter there.

14. November 1777. Approved by the Continental Congress, the Articles are America's first national constitution.

15. September 1777. General Howe's army defeats Washington's forces.

16. December 1777–June 1778. Continental Army suffers hunger, cold.

17. June 1778. Washington's army fights British Army led by General Henry Clinton to a standoff.

18. December 1778. British capture major southern city from American General Robert Howe.

19. May 1778. Crucial assistance; comes when news of the Saratoga victory reaches Paris.

20. July 1779. Joins in order to injure the enemy, Great Britain.

21. March–May 1780. Ends in overwhelming American defeat, with thousands of soldiers captured.

22. September 1780. Arnold flees from West Point, which he had planned to deliver to the British; becomes a general in the British Army.

23. September 1781. French naval fleet under the Comte de Grasse defeats British fleet, cutting off an escape from Yorktown via sea for Cornwallis.

24. September–October 1781. Cornwallis and British Army are caught in Yorktown, surrounded by French naval fleet, Washington's army, and French Army under Rochambeau.

25. October 1781. Cornwallis has no other option; the war is effectively over.

Mapping (page 27)

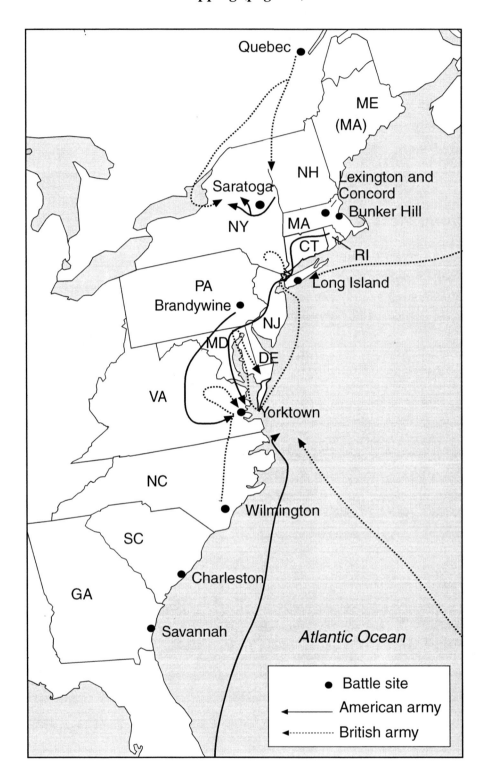

Battle Results (page 28)

1. <u>Accurate:</u> An inexperienced general, Washington did manage to withdraw his troops when near-certain capture was close, both from Long Island and then from Manhattan Island, thus keeping the Continental Army in existence.

2. <u>Not accurate:</u> Had Howe acted more decisively, he probably could have captured Washington and his army, thus crushing the infant rebellion.

3. <u>Accurate:</u> He did follow the plan, but Howe went to Philadelphia instead of meeting Burgoyne in Albany as he was supposed to do; St. Leger was slow to get started on his branch of the maneuver and then was defeated by Arnold's forces and driven back before he could meet with Burgoyne's army.

4. <u>Accurate:</u> The militiamen—informal soldiers at best, more civilian than military—twice beat back an attack by British regulars, the best soldiers in the world, and killed over a thousand of them. The Americans lost the battle only when they ran out of ammunition.

5. <u>Inaccurate:</u> He had no other choice. He couldn't retreat by sea once the French defeated the British fleet, and Washington and Rochambeau had him surrounded by land.

A Failed Plan (page 30)

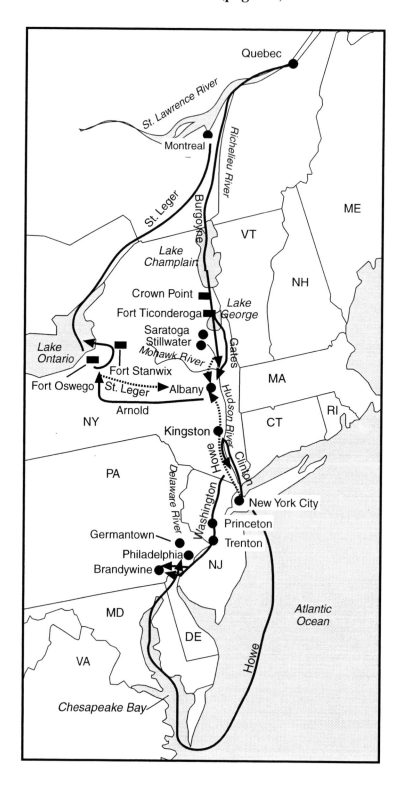

The Stars and Stripes (page 31)

Union Jack

White cross stands for: Scotland (cross of St. Andrew)
Red cross stands for: England (cross of St. George)
Together they stand for: the new union of England and Scotland
Date: 1606

New England Flag

Pine tree stands for: New England
Red cross stands for: England (cross of St. George)
Date: 1700's

Taunton Flag

Canton stands for: Great Britain (the Union Jack)
Where it flew: Taunton, Massachusetts
Date: 1774

Continental Navy Flag

Stripes stand for: the American states (13)
Where it flew: on ships of the Continental (American) Navy
Date: 1775

Continental Colors, or Grand Union Flag

Canton stands for: Great Britain (the Union Jack), "rights of Englishmen"
Stripes stand for: the American states (13)
Where it flew: on ships of the Continental Navy
Date: December 1775

Stars and Stripes

Canton stands for: "a new constellation"—the Union
Date: summer 1777

A Soldier's Life (page 32)

Among the hardships: illness; hunger, lack of sufficient food; cold; lack of sufficient clothing; poor food; uncomfortable, inadequate living quarters; fatigue; smoke-filled lodgings; lack of footwear; discouragement; skin itch; lice; physical punishment for breaking army rules; lack of pay; dreadful conditions as prisoner of war

The Opposing Armies (page 34)

Part 1

1. British, advantage
2. American, advantage
3. American, disadvantage
4. British, disadvantage
5. American, advantage
6. British, disadvantage
7. American, disadvantage
8. American, advantage
9. American, disadvantage
10. British, disadvantage
11. British, advantage
12. American, advantage
13. American, disadvantage
14. American, disadvantage

Part 2

1. Most of the war was fought on land, on the Americans' home turf; Americans didn't need to supply themselves via sea.

2. This fine base was thousands of miles away, across an ocean.

3. Many soldiers were enlisted instead of serving jail terms; oppressed lower-class people and men fighting for pay were much less motivated than the colonists, who were fighting for their homes, land, families, and freedom. Also, the British had to sail reinforcements all the way from Europe, while American militiamen were always available and often poured in when a battle began.

4. The British government was inefficient and poorly directed, with positions awarded according to privilege and favor.

Who Said It? (page 35)

1. Benjamin Franklin
2. James Otis
3. Captain John Parker
   (at Lexington)
4. Israel Putnam (Bunker Hill)
5. Patrick Henry
6. James Mugford (Boston)
7. Thomas Paine
8. Nathan Hale
9. John Paul Jones
10. John Hancock
11. Benjamin Franklin
12. Abigail Adams

Civilians in Wartime (page 36)

The Resources section of this book will be helpful in identifying sources of readings for the students for this activity.

The Allies (page 39)

France

1a. To weaken her enemy, Great Britain.

1b. To get back some of the territory she lost in the French and Indian (Seven Years') War; to deprive her enemy of profitable colonies.

1c. Secretly funneled supplies to the rebelling colonies; when France entered into a formal alliance, economic aid continued, and French land and naval forces fought against the British in the war.

Spain

2a. To injure her enemy, Great Britain.

2b. To gain lands in North America from the British.

2c. Sent supplies to the rebels; Spanish fought the British in Florida and for Gulf of Mexico ports.

Holland

3a. To injure her enemy, Great Britain.

3b. Trade advantages with the former colonies, without disadvantages imposed by British mercantile system.

3c. Sent aid (supplies, clothing, etc.).

Note: Neither Holland nor Spain became formal allies of the United States in the war.

Mapping the Peace (page 40)

Part 1

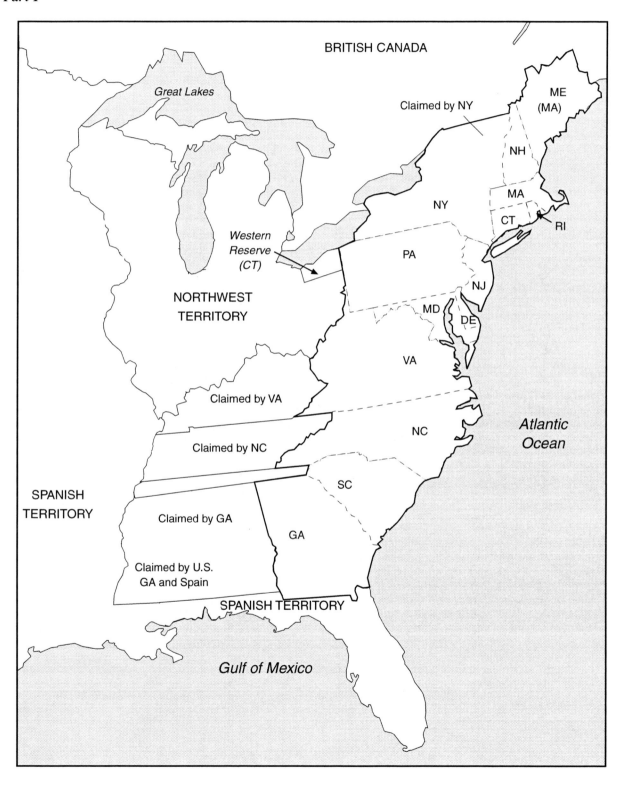

Mapping the Peace (page 40)

Part 2

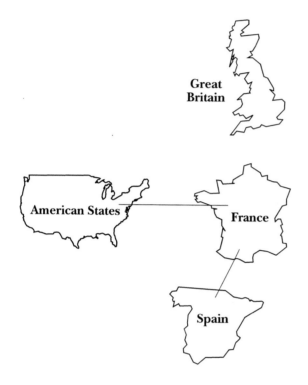

The War Ends: Another Treaty of Paris (page 41)

United States

<u>Territory gained:</u> Northwest Territory, eastern Mississippi Valley

<u>Effect on economic interests:</u> Loses advantageous trade position within British Empire; gains right to trade freely with all nations; vast new lands for economic expansion.

<u>Effect on strategic interests:</u> Gains generally peaceful, easy-to-defend boundaries, but still lacks guaranteed outlet at mouth of Mississippi River.

Native American nations

<u>Territory lost:</u> Northwest Territory and eastern Mississippi Valley are now part of the new nation of united states rather than under British control.

<u>Effect on economic interests:</u> Will lose their hunting, agricultural lands when white settlers move in.

<u>Effect on strategic interests:</u> British are no longer on hand to restrain whites eager to move into Indian lands across the Appalachians.

France

<u>Territory gained or lost:</u> None

<u>Effect on economic interests:</u> Enemy, Great Britain, is weakened by loss of profitable colonies; France can now trade freely with the former colonies.

<u>Effect on strategic interests:</u> A powerful enemy has been weakened.

Spain

<u>Territory gained:</u> Gets Florida from Great Britain, but fails to get the eastern Mississippi Valley (area from Appalachians west to Mississippi River).

<u>Effect on economic interests:</u> Gains economically from Florida's resources, opportunity to trade with former colonies.

<u>Effect on strategic interests:</u> Florida links westward to the Louisiana Territory, strengthening Spain's control of the Gulf of Mexico area; a powerful enemy, Great Britain, has been weakened; but Spain is thwarted in its desire to control lands west of Appalachians.

Great Britain

<u>Territory lost:</u> All of the former colonies, plus the Northwest Territory and the eastern Mississippi Valley, plus Florida—all are lost.

<u>Effect on economic interests:</u> Loses profitable colonies, but saves huge cost of administering them; can still profit from exporting manufactured goods to former colonies while holding imports from them to a minimum.

<u>Effect on strategic interests:</u> Loses colonies but puts a weak English-speaking nation in control of the eastern Mississippi Valley instead of either of its powerful enemies, France or Spain.

Additional Activity Suggestions

You could have students do any of the following activities.

1. Create an illustration of a typical American soldier, or minuteman. Do the same for a typical British soldier. Or, create an authentic American Revolutionary soldier or militiaman outfit that you can wear.

2. Map and describe the war on the western frontier involving Native Americans, frontier residents, and the George Rogers Clark expeditions.

3. Map and describe the naval engagements of the war.

4. Create a chart that explains how the colonies financed the Revolutionary War.

5. Write a paper describing what one major figure contributed to the war, and tell how you think the course of the war might have been different if that person hadn't been involved.

6. Visit a Revolutionary War historic site—one near where you live, if possible. Take photos and collect visitor brochures, maps, and other materials to create a class display of your visit. Present your display orally to the class.

Unit 2 Assessment

1. Describe the various advantages and disadvantages that both the Americans and the British brought to the war. How did these advantages and disadvantages play out in the course of the war? How were the Americans able to defeat the world's strongest empire?

2. Compare the Revolutionary War with the rebels' struggle for independence in the *Star Wars* trilogy.

Unit 3: Changing American Society

Native Americans and the Revolutionary Era (page 47)

Part 1

American allies: Catawba, Delaware, Oneida, Tuscarora (Delaware also sometimes were British allies)

British allies: Cherokee, Creek, Iroquois (Cayuga, Mohawk, Onondaga, Seneca), Miami, Ottawa

Part 2

Lord Dunmore's War

Native American groups: Shawnee, Mingo, Delaware
Native American leaders: Cornstalk, Logan
Site of victory: Point Pleasant (in present-day West Virginia)

Cherokee raids

States: Georgia, South Carolina, Tennessee

Wyoming Valley raids

Native American groups: Iroquois (with Loyalists), Delaware (with white settlers)
Wyoming massacre: Wyoming, Pennsylvania (northwestern Pennsylvania)

Cherry Valley massacre: Cherry Valley, New York

Sullivan's expedition

Native American groups: Iroquois
villages in northwestern Pennsylvania, New York

Who Was I? African-American Society (page 48)

1. Phillis Wheatley
2. Paul Cuffee
3. Elizabeth Freeman (Mumbet)
4. Prince Hall
5. Jupiter Hammon
6. Peter Salem
7. Benjamin Banneker
8. Lucy Prince Terry
9. Richard Allen or Absalom Jones
10. Crispus Attucks
11. Deborah Gannett
12. Gustavus Vassa (Olaudah Equiano)

Women in Revolutionary America (page 49)

1. h
2. j
10. p
11. o

3. g
4. i
5. l
12. e
13. b
14. d

6. n   15. f

7. m   16. a

8. q   17. k

9. c

The Rights of Women (page 50)

1. <u>Liberative new ideas:</u> Women should have the right to vote; they have the right to have representation in the law-making assembly. Women need access to good education and need to exercise their minds.

2. <u>Limiting traditional ideas:</u> Husbands rule their wives; women need to be educated in order to fulfill their roles as mothers, instructing their children on becoming responsible citizens.

An American National Spirit (page 53)

Sample examples:

Education: Noah Webster's *The American Spelling Book* and his *Reader* (featuring speeches of Revolutionary leaders); John M'Culloch's American history textbook; change in name of King's College to Columbia

Religion: Anglican Church becomes Protestant Episcopal church; Dutch and German Reformed churches became independent American churches; Roman Catholics get an American bishop

Painting: Many examples, from artists such as John Trumbull and John Vanderlyn

Literature: Mercy Otis Warren's history of the Revolution; Joel Barlow's poems and his *Vision of Columbus*

Architecture: the Greco-Roman style, emphasizing republicanism—Monticello, the Virginia state capitol building, and the U.S. Capitol are examples

Drama: Royall Tyler's play *The Contrast*

Science: Jedidiah Morse's popular *American Geography;* founding of American Academy of Arts and Sciences

Additional Activity Suggestions

You could have students do any of the following activities.

1. Learn more about young people's experiences during the Revolutionary era by reading historical fiction and primary sources like *Becoming American* (see Resources section).

2. Debate in class whether Abigail Adams's declaration to her husband that "the ladies . . . will not hold ourselves bound by any laws in which we have no voice, or representation" is as valid as the colonists' arguments against "taxation without representation."

3. Write a thorough report on the role of one or several Native American nations in the Revolutionary War. How did the Revolution ultimately affect Native Americans?

4. Write a report on the role of African-Americans in the Revolutionary War, and the effect of the Revolution on blacks in America.

5. Write a biography of one of the African-Americans named in the Who Was I? activity or of another black person of the Revolutionary era.

Unit 3 Assessment

Assess the American Revolution's effect on American society. Did it bring about revolutionary changes? How did it affect various groups? What changes did it cause in social, political, and economic conditions?

Unit 4: Creating New Governments

Mapping the New Nation (page 62)

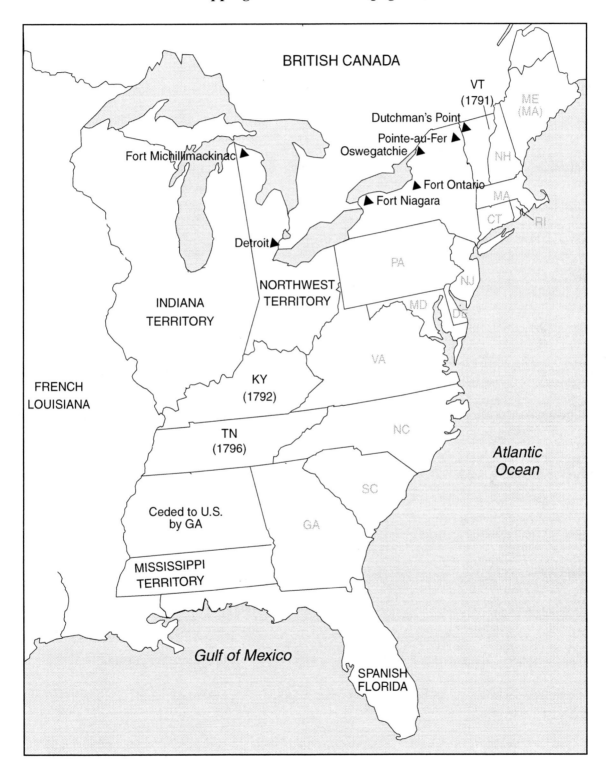

Questions:

1. The British had a string of forts all along the border with Canada and the United States, keeping a threatening military presence.

2. Jay's Treaty

The Articles of Confederation (page 63)

National government powers: Determine peace and war; send and receive ambassadors; enter into treaties and alliances; decide disputes between states; fix weights and measures; regulate relations with Indians; establish and run national post offices; appoint army and navy officers; establish and regulate national armed forces.

State power: Everything not given to national government; the most important are the right to raise taxes, regulate commerce, and issue money—these caused great problems for the nation as a whole.

The Northwest Ordinance (page 64)

Here are the words from the Ordinance; use your discretion in asking students either to use their own words or to quote directly from the Ordinance.

1. **Practice of religion**—Article 1: No person, demeaning himself in a peaceable and orderly manner, shall ever be molested on account of his mode of worship or religious sentiments, in the said territory.

2. **Justice system**—Article 2: The inhabitants of the said territory shall always be entitled to the benefits of the writ of *habeas corpus*, and of the trial by jury; of a proportionate representation of the people in the legislature; and of judicial proceedings according to the course of the common law. All persons shall be bailable, unless for capital offences, where the proof shall be evident or the presumption great. All fines shall be moderate; and no cruel or unusual punishments shall be inflicted. No man shall be deprived of his liberty or property, but by the judgment of his peers or the law of the land; and, should the public exigencies make it necessary, for the common preservation to take any person's property, or to demand his particular services, full compensation shall be made for the same. And, in the just preservation of rights and property, it is understood and declared, that no law ought ever to be made, or have force in the said territory, that shall, in any manner whatever, interfere with or affect private contracts or engagements, *bona fide*, and without fraud, previously formed.

3. **Status of slavery**—Article 6: There shall be neither slavery nor involuntary servitude in the said teritory, otherwise than in the punishment of crimes whereof the party shall have been duly convicted. *Provided always,* That any person escaping into the same, from whom labor or service is lawfully claimed in any one of the original states, such fugitive may be lawfully reclaimed and conveyed to the person claiming his or her labor or service as aforesaid.

4. **Education**—Article 3: Religion, morality, and knowledge, being necessary to good government and the happiness of mankind, schools and the means of education shall forever be encouraged.

5. **Relations with Native Americans**—Article 3: The utmost good faith shall always be observed towards the Indians; their lands and property shall never be taken from them without their consent; and, in their property, rights, and liberty, they shall never be invaded or disturbed, unless in just and lawful wars authorized by Congress; but laws founded in justice and humanity, shall from time to time be made for preventing wrongs being done to them, and for preserving peace and friendship with them.

6. **The Bill of Rights**

7. Poorly; white appetite for lands always overcame consideration and fair treatment for Native Americans.

Postwar Economic Woes (page 66)

<u>British stop ordering American ships:</u> Northern merchants want national commerce powers.

<u>Very high state taxes:</u> Shays's Rebellion; need for strong central government to suppress it and to raise revenues.

<u>Congress can't pay national debt or wages owed to war veterans:</u> Need tariffs on imports to raise money; but one state (Rhode Island) was able to veto this, so need a change from unanimous rule required in Articles of Confederation.

<u>Crop failures, cash shortages:</u> Add to unrest, economic woes—need for a stronger national government to stabilize the economy.

<u>States tax one another's goods:</u> Need a national government that can regulate interstate commerce.

<u>States print paper money:</u> Adds to economic unbalances; need a national government that can control currency.

<u>British manufactured goods flood United States:</u> Need a national government that can impose import taxes to force change in British trade policies.

<u>Plantation labor shortage:</u> Happened because of British slave taking during the war; need a central government to force changes in British trade policies.

<u>British duty on rice, etc.:</u> Again, need a central government that can impose import duties to force changes in British policies.

<u>West Indies trade:</u> Same as above.

The Slavery Debate (page 69)

Pro: Rebellions aren't a problem; other states don't need to help southern states if slave rebellions do occur; states have a right to protect their property interests in slavery and the slave trade—religion and humanity are irrelevant concerns here; importing slaves profits shipping interests; supporting slaves increases economic consumption overall; what enriches one part of the country is a benefit to the whole country.

Con: Slavery and the slave trade are inhumane, contrary to the principles of honor the nation is based upon; slavery curses the states where it exists and will bring the wrath of heaven on those states; including slaves in representation count is unfair and horrifying to states without large slave populations and encourages importing more slaves; nonslave states will be forced to protect slave states when slaves rebel; slave labor discourages free laborers from engaging in artisan and manufacturing jobs; slave masters are tyrants; it is unfair to tax all imports except slaves.

Middle ground: Every state has a right to import what it wants; morality or wisdom of slavery is up to each individual state; slavery will eventually become obsolete, unneeded, and economically unfeasible anyway; let slave states keep this so the Constitution can be approved.

Challenge Question: George Mason was the convention's largest slaveholder, yet he spoke fiercely against slavery.

Separation of Powers (page 71)

Part 1

1. Legislative (Senate)
2. Legislative
3. Executive
4. Judiciary
5. Executive
6. Legislative
7. Judiciary
8. Executive
9. Legislative

Part 2

1. <u>Executive:</u> If he [the President of the United States] approve [a bill] he shall sign it, but if not he shall return it, with his objections, to that house in which it shall have originated.

2. <u>Legislative:</u> The Congress shall have power to lay and collect taxes, duties, imposts and excises.

3. <u>Judiciary</u>: The judicial power shall extend to all cases, in law and equity . . . between citizens of different states.

4. <u>Legislative</u>: To raise and support armies . . . To provide and maintain a navy.

5. <u>Executive</u>: The President shall be Commander in Chief of the army and navy of the United States.

Checks and Balances (page 72)

1. Right to declare war, raise money for armed forces

2. Presidential veto power

3. Right to approve treaties

4. Right to override veto

5. Right to approve appointments

6. Right to impeach

7. Right of judicial review

The Fine Art of Compromise (page 73)

Slave Trade

<u>Actual compromise:</u> No ban on importation can be imposed by Congress before 1808.

Exports

<u>Actual compromise:</u> Export taxes were prohibited (southern states wanted this) in exchange for southern states dropping their demand that laws regulating foreign commerce and navigation would require a two-thirds majority vote.

Imports

<u>Actual compromise:</u> Southerners accepted tax on imports of slaves in return for no immediate ban on slave trade or ban on slavery itself.

Federalists and Anti-Federalists (page 74)

2. Richard Henry Lee was from an aristocratic Virginia family, the type of background that usually produced Federalists. Alexander Hamilton was from a humble background—his father deserted the family—and was a self-made man, definitely not the type you'd expect to be a leader of the wealthy aristocratic Federalists.

Positions and Population (page 75)

1. More populous states, because they'd have more representatives (e.g., Maryland, New York, North Carolina, Pennsylvania, Virginia, Massachusetts)

2. Small states, so they'd have equal representation in spite of population (e.g., Delaware, Rhode Island, New Jersey, New Hampshire)

3. Middle-range states in population—no decisive advantage in either direction (e.g., Connecticut, South Carolina)

4. States with large slave populations (e.g., Maryland, North Carolina, South Carolina, Virginia)

5. States without large slave populations, who wanted slaves to be included in the taxable population count for slave-holding states (e.g., Delaware, New England states, Rhode Island, Pennsylvania)

Additional Activity Suggestions

You could have students do any of the following activities.

1. Read more about the constitutional convention. Make a chart of the many difficult issues delegates wrestled with, showing each issue, the different positions of various interest groups on the issue, and the compromise the delegates finally achieved on that issue.

2. Role-play a debate between a debt-ridden Massachusetts farmer who is taking part in Shays's Rebellion and the wealthy creditor he or she owes money to.

3. Compare your state's constitution with the U.S. Constitution. What similarities and differences do you find? What powers does your state legislature have or not have that the national congress has? your state executive? your state judiciary? Does your state constitution include a bill of rights? If not, should it? Does your state constitution have as many, fewer, or more amendments than the U.S. Constitution?

4. Write brief biographies of four or five leading Federalists and anti-Federalists. Relate events in their lives to their political positions.

5. Identify elements of anti-Federalist positions in a recent U.S. presidential election campaign.

Unit 4 Assessment

1. Discuss the accomplishments and failures of government under the Articles of Confederation. [This could take the form of a class discussion or debate.]

2. Analyze the U.S. Constitution and the process by which it was created to explain why a document so old continues to work so well in modern times.

Unit 5: Fine-tuning The System

The Bill of Rights (page 81)

Part 1

Amendment 1: Freedom of religion, freedom of speech, freedom of press, right to assemble and petition about grievances

Amendment 2: Right to keep and bear arms

Amendment 4: Freedom from unreasonable searches and seizures; searches only with warrants obtained on specific information

Amendment 8: No excessive bail, no excessive fines, no cruel or unusual punishment

Part 2

1. No. Amendment 5: "nor shall any person be subject for the same offense to be twice put in jeopardy of life or limb"

2. Being arrested and held in jail for indefinite periods of time with no specific charges made; being tried without an impartial jury, in secret, without being able to confront witnesses against yourself, call witnesses for yourself, or have a defense lawyer

3. Having to feed and house alien soldiers, under the Quartering Act passed by Parliament

4. No. Amendment 5: "nor shall be compelled in any criminal case to be a witness against himself"

5. Amendment 5 (Fifth Amendment): "nor be deprived of life, liberty, or property, without due process of law"

Why a Bill of Rights? (page 84)

1. Because the Constitution didn't specifically protect individual rights; because federal laws under the Constitution are "the supreme law of the land"—so amendments are necessary to spell out what areas this "supreme law" can't touch, and so states' powers are specifically reserved to them.

2. Because numerous provisions within the Constitution do mention particular privileges and rights of citizens that are protected; because you don't need to say that certain freedoms can't be violated when in fact there is no power under the Constitution to limit those freedoms.

The Sedition Act (page 85)

1. It seems that the act violates freedom of speech and of the press when it says people can't write, print, utter, or publish "any false, scandalous and malicious writings . . . with intent to . . . bring [government bodies or officials] into contempt or disrepute . . . or to resist, oppose, or defeat any [federal] law or act."

2. Federalists wanted to suppress anti-Federalist criticism coming from Republican newspapers, especially from radical immigrants who criticized Federalist foreign policy.

3. Anti-French feeling fanned by the XYZ affair prompted conservative Federalists to view the foreign policy criticisms as disloyal.

Hamilton versus Jefferson (page 86)

Strict versus loose interpretation of Constitution

Hamilton: Favored a loose interpretation of the Constitution's elastic clause about making all "necessary and proper" laws; Congress could act whenever it was "proper."

Jefferson: Favored a strict interpretation of the Constitution's elastic clause; Congress should act only when "necessary."

National bank

Hamilton: Wanted Congress to charter one, sell some of its stock to individuals; this would be good for investors in the bank.

Jefferson: A national bank is not "necessary," so it is not authorized under the Constitution; such a bank would benefit commercial classes, not the farmers Jefferson favored.

Paying the national war debt

Hamilton: Fund it at par via new bonds; pay security holders in full; benefits well-to-do security holders and commercial interests.

Jefferson: Initially opposed; ordinary citizens had loaned the government money and then had to sell the securities at a deep discount to speculators—wanted these people at least partially repaid. Accepted Hamilton's plan in exchange for the national capital city being situated on the Potomac River.

The American economy

Hamilton: Stressed manufacturing, commerce, finance.

Jefferson: Wanted a simple agrarian economy.

British society and government

Hamilton: Admired both; liked the orderliness of the British government and financial systems.

Jefferson: Disliked both; thought British society was decadent, the government corrupt and anti-republican.

France's revolution

Hamilton: Abhorred the violence and social disruptions of the French Revolution.

Jefferson: Admired France's republican revolution.

The central government

Hamilton: Favored a strong central government.

Jefferson: Favored states' rights.

Which Political Party? (page 87)

Remind students they can be black or white, male or female.

The Rebellions: A Closer Look (page 89)

Political factors

Shays' Rebellion: Western common people versus commercial-oriented state legislature

Whiskey Rebellion: Western Republicans versus Federalists, national government.

Economic factors

Shays' Rebellion: Western agrarians versus eastern moneyed interests

Whiskey Rebellion: Farmers versus commercial interests

Social factors

Shays' Rebellion: Farmers, people of moderate means, versus state politicians insensitive to the effect of fiscal policies on common people

Whiskey Rebellion: Farmers feeling unfairly targeted by Federalists mostly concerned about well-to-do people of commerce

Geographic factors

Shays' Rebellion: Western farmers versus eastern moneyed interests and politicians

Whiskey Rebellion: Western farmers versus urban centers, national government to the east

Supreme Court Power (page 90)

Marbury v. Madison

Summary: Marbury petitioned the Supreme Court to order the secretary of state to give him his commission as a justice of the peace, issued under the Judiciary Act of 1801.

Decision: Marbury's request was made under a provision of the Judiciary Act that was unconstitutional and therefore void.

Increase in Supreme Court power: The Supreme Court can now strike down a law passed by Congress.

McCulloch v. Maryland

Summary: The Maryland legislature passed a law taxing "foreign banks" and demanded that McCulloch, treasurer of the Bank of the United States, pay the tax. McCulloch refused.

Decision: The Bank of the United States was legally created, justified by the implied constitutional powers of Congress, so Maryland can't try to destroy it by taxation.

Increase in Supreme Court power: Supreme Court can restrain state as well as national laws.

Increase in national power: Congress can act on implied powers; has wide latitude under this Hamiltonian "loose" interpretation of the Constitution; national economy is aided also.

Gibbons v. Ogden

Summary: Ogden operated a New York–New Jersey steamboat line under a New York monopoly. He sued Gibbons for setting up a competing line.

Decision: A state can't make laws regulating interstate commerce.

Increase in Supreme Court power: Confirms Court's power to strike down state laws.

Increase in national power: Supremacy of federal power over state power in the area of interstate commerce is confirmed.

Treaty Making (page 91)

Treaty of Greenville (1795)

Between United States and Native Americans fighting in Ohio country (Shawnee, Miami, Wyandot, Potwatomi, Ottawa)

United States gains: Indians cede two-thirds of Ohio state area, parts of Indiana and other northwest territory

Treaty of Fort Stanwix (1784)

Between United States and Iroquois Nation

United States gains: Iroquois give up claims to western New York, Pennsylvania, Ohio

Pinckney's Treaty (1795)

Formal name: Treaty of San Lorenzo

Between United States and Spain

United States gains: Free navigation of Mississippi River; right of deposit at New Orleans; acceptance of U.S.-claimed boundary with Spanish Florida

Jay's Treaty (1795)

Between United States and Great Britain

United States gains: British agree to abandon forts along United States border with Canada

Review Questions

1. The executive

2. The Senate

Additional Activity Suggestions

You could have students do any of the following activities.

1. Some people were found guilty under the Sedition Act. Find out who they were and what they said or printed that got them in trouble. Do you find anything said or printed today that's as "false, scandalous and malicious" as what these people said?

2. Role-play arguing one of the famous cases before the Supreme Court and Chief Justice Marshall.

3. With classmates, create an ongoing class display of news articles, photographs, cartoons, and other materials illustrating the role of the Bill of Rights in today's life.

4. Stage a classroom "presidential debate" in which representatives of the media and the people ask a leading Federalist and a leading Republican questions on prominent issues.

5. Create a political pamphlet "written" by Thomas Jefferson and James Madison urging people to join their new political party and giving all the reasons why they should do so.

6. Create a chart that shows the impact of Alexander Hamilton's economic policies on different regions of the new nation.

Unit 5 Assessment

1. Explain the most important basic guarantees of the Bill of Rights. Discuss in detail the one you think is most important, describing its historical role and its importance today.

2. The Extra Challenge Hamilton-Jefferson role-play in the *Hamilton versus Jefferson* activity would make a good assessment vehicle for individual students.

ADDITIONAL RESOURCES

Historical Fiction for Students

Collier, James Lincoln, and Christopher Collier
(novels set in the Revolutionary era)
The Bloody Country (frontier conflict in the
Wyoming Valley west of Pennsylvania).
My Brother Sam Is Dead (a Connecticut family
divided in the Revolutionary War).
Jump Ship to Freedom (a 14-year-old runaway
slave).
War Comes to Willy Freeman (a young black girl
copes with the loss of her parents).
The Winter Hero (Shays's Rebellion).

Clapp, Patricia. *I'm Deborah Sampson: A Soldier in the
War of the Revolution.*

Fast, Howard. *April Morning* (the battle of Lexington
and Concord).

Finlayson, Ann. *Rebecca's War* (the British occupation
of Philadelphia).

Forbes, Esther. *Johnny Tremain* (Paul Revere's
helper).

Fritz, Jean. *Early Thunder* (Salem, 1775).

Koch, Betty. *Beyond the Allegheny.*

O'Dell, Scott. *Sarah Bishop* (young woman during the
Revolutionary War).

Roberts, Kenneth. *Rabble in Arms* (classic adult novel
of the Revolutionary War).

Nonfiction for Students

*Almanacs of American Life, Book 3: Revolutionary Amer-
ica, 1763–1800.* Facts on File.

Brenner, Barbara. *If You Were There in 1776.*

Dalgliesh, Alice. *Fourth of July Story.*

Fritz, Jean. Many highly praised historical biographies of Revolutionary era figures such as Paul

Revere, Samuel Adams, Patrick Henry, John
Hancock, and Benjamin Franklin.

Levy, Elizabeth. *If You Were There When They Signed the
Constitution.*

Peterson, Helen. *Give Us Liberty: The Story of the Declaration of Independence.*

Zall, Paul, ed. *Becoming American: Young People in the
American Revolution.*

Collections of Primary Source Documents: Print

*The Annals of America, Vol. 2, 1755–1783, Resistance
and Revolution* and *Vol. 3, Organizing the New
Nation.* Chicago: Encyclopedia Britannica, 1968.

Commager, Henry Steele, ed. *Documents of American
History,* 9th ed. (2 vols.). Englewood Cliffs, NJ:
Prentice-Hall, 1973.

Craven, Avery, Walter Johnson, and F. Roger Dunn. *A
Documentary History of the American People.* Boston:
Ginn and Company, 1951.

Hart, Albert Bushnell. *American History as Told by
Contemporaries* (5 volumes). New York: The
Macmillan Company, 1901.

Historical Abstracts of the United States. Washington,
DC: U.S. Department of Commerce, Bureau
of the Census, 1975.

MacDonald, William, ed. *Select Charters and Other
Documents Illustrative of American History 1606–
1775.* New York: The Macmillan Company, 1899.

Miller, Marion Mills, ed. *Great Debates in American
History,* Vol. 1 (Colonial Rights—The Revolution—The Constitution). New York: Current
Literature Publishing Company, 1913 (14
volumes in all).

CD-ROM

America Adventure. Knowledge Adventure (also available as a DOS floppy disk).

American Journey—History in Your Hands: The American Revolution. Research Publications.

American Journey—History in Your Hands: Women in America. Research Publications.

CD Sourcebook of American History. InfoBases.

Landmark Documents in American History. Facts on File (dwarfs the print collections).

World Wide Web/Internet

Sites with Numerous Links to U.S. History Sources:

Government/Social Studies Sources (includes listings of Library of Congress exhibits, historical documents from Project Gutenburg, other social studies Web sites):
http://www.nwoca.ohio.gov/www/gov.html

History/Social Studies Web Site for K–12 Teachers (includes site map, What's New Archive, sources arranged by category):
http://www.execpc.com/~dboals/boals.html

Library of Congress home page (includes American Memory historical collections):
http://lcweb.loc.gov

Kathy Schrock's site (a Cape Cod teacher's excellent list of resources):
http://www.capecod.net/schrockguide

U.S. Historic Documents (primary documents in full text):
http://www.ukans.edu/carrie/docs/amdocs_index.html

GLOSSARY

alien—a person living in one country who was born in a different country and is still a citizen of a foreign nation.

anti-Federalist—person who opposed the proposed U.S. Constitution.

boycott—an organized refusal to deal with a person, country, or business.

canton—the square in the upper left corner of a flag.

checks and balances—system in which each branch of government checks (holds back) the power of the other branches; one branch's powers are balanced by the other branches' powers.

colony—a territory that is tied to a parent state that controls it.

compromise—to come to an agreement by each side giving in on some points.

confederation—a group of states or nations united for mutual support and common action.

constitution—a written document that sets down the basic principles, laws, and rights of a nation and its people.

executive—the branch of government that executes (carries into effect) the laws and runs public affairs.

exports—goods sent out of a country or colony to another country or colony.

Federalist—person who supported the proposed U.S. Constitution.

grievance—a formal complaint; a cause of distress that calls for resistance or complaint.

imports—goods shipped into a country or colony from another country or colony.

judicial review—the principle that the federal courts can examine laws passed by Congress and decide if any law violates the U.S. Constitution; the court declares any such law invalid.

judiciary—the system of courts of law ; the branch of government that has the power to try cases and administer justice.

legislature—the body of government that has the power to make laws.

Loyalist—person of the Revolutionary War era who thought the British colonies should remain tied to England.

mercenary—a soldier who fights for a foreign country for pay.

militia—armed forces that are called up only during emergencies.

nationalism—loyalty and devotion to a country or nation.

navigation—the method of getting ships from place to place.

ordinance—law.

Parliament—the legislative body of England, which ruled the country and its colonies, along with the king.

Patriot—person of the Revolutionary War era who thought the British colonies should split from England.

ratify—to approve formally, as in ratifying a treaty.

"rights of Englishmen"—liberties for all free English persons that the king (or queen) or Parliament couldn't take away.

sedition—promoting resistance to or rebellion against lawful authority.

separation of powers—system in which the main branches of government are separate from one another; each branch has its own powers.

tariff—a set of taxes on imported goods.

treaty—a formal agreement between two (or more) nations.

writ of assistance—general search warrant.

Notes

Share Your Bright Ideas with Us!

We want to hear from you! Your valuable comments and suggestions will help meet your current and future classroom needs.

Your name_____Date_____

School name_____Phone_____

School address_____

Grade level taught_____Subject area(s) taught_____Average class size_

Where did you purchase this publication?_____

Was your salesperson knowledgeable about this product?   Yes_____   No_____

What monies were used to purchase this product?

_____School supplemental budget   _____Federal/state funding   _____Personal

Please "grade" this Walch publication according to the following criteria:

	A	B	C	D	F
Quality of service you received when purchasing	A	B	C	D	F
Ease of use	A	B	C	D	F
Quality of content	A	B	C	D	F
Page layout	A	B	C	D	F
Organization of material	A	B	C	D	F
Suitability for grade level	A	B	C	D	F
Instructional value	A	B	C	D	F

COMMENTS:_____

_____

What specific supplemental materials would help you meet your current—or future—instructional needs?

_____

Have you used other Walch publications? If so, which ones?_____

May we use your comments in upcoming communications?   ____Yes   ____No

Please **FAX** this completed form to **207-772-3105**, or mail it to:

Product Development, J. Weston Walch, Publisher, P.O. Box 658, Portland, ME 04104-0658